# KITCHEN SINK
## SCIENCE

# KITCHEN SINK
# SCIENCE

## INCREDIBLE EXPERIMENTS
## WITH EVERYDAY OBJECTS

### ROB BEATTIE

**METRO BOOKS**
New York

**METRO BOOKS**
New York

An Imprint of Sterling Publishing
1166 Avenue of the Americas
New York, NY 10036

ISBN 978-1-4351-6992-0

For information about custom editions, special sales, and premium
and corporate purchases, please contact Sterling Special Sales
at 800-805-5489 or specialsales@sterlingpublishing.com.

Manufactured in China

2 4 6 8 10 9 7 5 3 1

sterlingpublishing.com


Design, illustration, and image editing by Amazing15

"In France, a chemist named Pilâtre de Rozier tested the flammability of hydrogen by gulping a mouthful and blowing across an open flame, proving at a stroke that hydrogen is indeed explosively combustible and that eyebrows are not necessarily a permanent feature of one's face."

**—Bill Bryson, *A Short History of Nearly Everything***

**Don't try this at home!**

# CONTENTS

## PART 1

# MYSTERIOUS MOTION

## PART 2

# FANTASTIC FORCES

# INTRODUCTION

Well, hello there. We're so excited to welcome you to the only science book your kitchen will ever need. Pull up a chair, and we'll explain what's going on and what you can expect from this book.

First and foremost, **FUN**. For people of a certain age, learning about science wasn't always fun. In fact, it was the opposite: it was unfun. This book puts the X factor back into eXperiments, and it's our intention to lead you on an entertaining ride around many different subjects, substances, and phenomena. Along the way you'll discover some of the amazing properties of the stuff you've got on your kitchen shelves or hidden away in that cupboard under the sink, as well as how combining different "ingredients" can make them even more remarkable.

Next up, **FACTS**. Of course, science is also a serious and fascinating subject, and there'll be plenty of facts to back up the individual experiments, so you can understand the principles at work in each one. There may even be the odd—and some of them are very odd—history lesson along the way.

Finally, we didn't forget about **FROTH**. Of course, there'll be *plenty* of foam, fizz, and splatter in these experiments.

For ease, we've broken the experiments down into broad categories. The first, **MYSTERIOUS MOTION**, is all about things that move: why they move, how they move, and the science behind that movement.

A lot of the time, the forces that make the world turn are invisible. In the second section, **FANTASTIC FORCES**, the experiments focus on some of the most fascinating examples of push and pull.

What happens when you mix A with B and maybe chuck in little X, Y, and Z? The third section, **MARVELOUS MIXTURES**, is where you'll find out.

One of science's central themes is the way in which the universe—even the stuff in your kitchen—is constantly changing. The experiments in the final section, **TERRIFIC TRANSITIONS**, will help you to understand why.

There's bound to be a bit of overlap across the sections—after all, although it's a precise subject, science is no respecter of boundaries. It's also part of what makes the whole thing such a hoot.

Ok, we've set the scene. Now let's take a closer look at how the experiments are set out and talk a bit about what you can expect.

# ABOUT THIS BOOK

There are **45 experiments** in this book and the idea behind each one is the same: to take the kind of stuff you've likely already got hanging around in your kitchen and use it to create interesting and entertaining experiments that demonstrate scientific principles.

In order to achieve this, each experiment has the same basic structure.

**YOU WILL NEED:** Here we'll list the items required to carry out each experiment. You'll probably already have most of the items here. Occasionally you'll have to buy something, but it'll only cost a few dollars and we think it'll be worth it.

**SETUP:** Here's where we talk you through how to put the experiment together. This might involve intertwining forks, mixing vinegar (there's a lot of vinegar!) with other ingredients, putting things in the freezer, taking them out again… you get the idea.

**TESTING** Here's the fun part. Having assembled everything you need for the experiment and then put it all together, you now get to see what happens. Sometimes you'll be able to guess in advance but often it'll be a complete surprise.

**ADDITIONAL SETUP:** If an experiment has variations or alternatives that will help you dive deeper and discover more, you'll find them here.

**IN CONCLUSION:** This is where we'll explain what's going on "behind the scenes" in the experiment. We might talk about how the scientific principles are used in the real world and look back to the early pioneers who first observed or discovered it.

**OTHER STUFF:** To ensure that you and your family are safe, we've provided notes on a few sensible precautions (page 10). You can also read about the equipment you're likely to need (page 12) and how to go about setting up your experiments (page 14). At the back of the book, check out the glossary of key scientific terms (page 154) and some leads on where else to look for kitchen-based science fun (page 156).

## PUZZLER!?!

THROUGHOUT THE BOOK YOU'LL ALSO FIND PUZZLERS TO TEST YOUR SCIENTIFIC KNOWLEDGE. FOR THE ANSWERS, TURN TO PAGE 157.

### IMPORTANT: FAKE SCIENCE

In an age where accusations of "fake news" abound, we thought we'd join in. So, one of the experiments included in the book is bogus. It's a fake, a phoney and, no matter how carefully you follow the instructions, **it will not work**. It's hidden in plain sight, somewhere in the book, and we come clean on those same pages, so at least you'll know when you've been taken for a ride.

# SAFETY

Here at the Institute of Kitchen Sink Science we take your safety very seriously—and so should you. Fortunately, most of the experiments in this book don't involve anything particularly dangerous. We're not in the business of showing you how to blow things up (unless they're balloons), make things that are going to stink out the house, or set the place on fire.

We do, however, ask that you observe basic safety principles. And while most of these are common sense, it's worth setting them out here so we're all on the same page—the "keeping you safe" page.

### THINGS THAT CUT

There aren't many knives used in these experiments but, where there are, they usually need to be sharp. Always cut away from your other hand. If you're cutting through something, watch out for whatever's underneath it. Keep knives away from kids, your eyes—any body parts, in fact. Just be sensible.

### THINGS THAT FLY

Don't stand in front of anything that's about to fly through the air and especially don't lean into the line of fire while you're trying to work out why something hasn't taken off. We don't think there's anything in the book that's strong enough to do any damage to your kitchen, but it's always best to behave as if it could.

### THINGS YOU SET ON FIRE AND THINGS THAT GET VERY HOT OR VERY COLD

Treat any experiment that includes the words "fire," "heat," "stove," "boil," "bubbling," "steam," "smoke," "ash," and so on with even more respect than usual. No one wants to be jumping up and down and shouting "Eureka!" while running their hand under the cold tap.

And speaking of cold, there are several experiments that require you to take something out of the freezer which—by definition—means they are likely to be frozen. Grabbing a frozen bottle like the handlebars of a bike could result in a nasty burn, so be careful when handling anything icy.

### THINGS THAT REACT AGGRESSIVELY

The main thing to watch out for here is mess. If you don't follow the instructions carefully and just slosh a load of extra X or Y into a mixture, your cup may literally runneth over and damage your kitchen table or countertop.

## THINGS THAT SMELL INTERESTING

Don't consume anything in this book. Just don't. (As always, though, there's one exception: see page 72).

## SAFETY EQUIPMENT

You should have a basic home first aid kit anyway, which will allow you to deal with most mishaps. We don't anticipate you'll need a fire extinguisher for any experiments, but when fire's involved, have water on hand just in case.

## KIDS AND THESE EXPERIMENTS

We encourage scientific exploration at almost any age. Adults will have lots of fun doing these experiments with kids, and can keep an eye on them while you're working together. If you're comfortable with a young person doing any of these experiments on their own, please make sure they understand the "rules of the road" and carry out the experiments responsibly. Even a splash of household vinegar in the eye is going to sting like a bee.

## ADULTS AND THESE EXPERIMENTS

Don't try doing any of the experiments in the book if you're tired, on any kind of medication that impairs your judgement, or have just finished a large, relaxing glass of wine and think that trying out a gigantic version of the floating-teabags-that-are-on-fire (see pages 20–23) is a good idea. It isn't!

## SYMBOLS AND WHAT THEY MEAN

 Where we think an experiment demands extra care or has a mild element of danger, you'll see it clearly marked with a DANGER symbol.

 Where we feel there's a chance you're going to create an unholy mess, you'll see the experiment clearly marked with a MESSY symbol.

# EQUIPMENT

Here's a rundown of the kind of special scientific equipment you're going to need to carry out the experiments in this book. Every item used in this book is of laboratory-grade standard, which means it's expensive and only available from specialist scientific suppliers. We know there's a chance that will put some readers off, but if you want the best results you have to use the best equipment.

Just kidding! With any luck you won't have to buy anything in order to enjoy this book to the full, or rather, with a couple of exceptions, you'll be buying the kind of stuff you'd be picking up in the supermarket or at the drugstore anyway.

Here's a quick guide to the kind of stuff you'll need to have on hand.

## HOUSEHOLD APPLIANCES

Vacuum cleaner with a nozzle
Hair dryer
Freezer
Stove
Barbecue lighter
Iron

## CRAFT SUPPLIES

Pens and pencils
Ruler
Craft sticks
Craft knife
Scissors
Sticky tape
Rubber bands
Glue
Hole punch
Tissue paper
Pushpins
Balloons
Plastic twine (or fishing line)
Paperclips

## PROVISIONS

Rice
Cornstarch
Teabags
Eggs
Sugar
Salt
Baking soda
Oranges
Lemons
Apples
Honey
Cereal fortified with iron
Peanut butter
Milk
Iceberg lettuce
Food dye
Alum (see page 100)
Water
Ice
Vegetable oil
Alka-Seltzer tablets
White vinegar

## HOUSEHOLD SUPPLIES

Drinking glasses

Glass jars

Glass bottles

Cups

Pyrex beakers

Turkey baster

Mixing bowls

Styrofoam™ plates and bowls

Cutlery

Measuring spoon

Metal tongs

Screwdriver

Potato masher

Sieve or strainer

Plastic lunchbox

Plastic bottles of various sizes

Plastic cups

Plates

Q-tips

Dish soap

Open-top freezer bags

Playing cards

Paper towels

Dish towel

Tinfoil

Matches or a lighter

Sewing needles

Empty toilet paper rolls

Empty soda cans

Saucepans

Wooden utensils

Toothpicks

Shoeboxes

Terra-cotta plant pots

Barbecue coals

Gardening gloves

Wooden skewers

Cookie cutters

An LP (record)

Black garbage bags

## MISCELLANEOUS

Coins

Candles of various sizes

Paper

Newspaper

Flashlight

Batteries

Round neodymium magnets

Ping-pong balls

Large teddy bear

Sand

Lighter fluid

Climbing plant in a little pot

Smartphone

Magnifying glass

Safety goggles (or cycling glasses if you don't have any)

Copper wire

As you can see, the only items you're very unlikely to have knocking around the house already are the neodymium magnets, and these can be picked up online for a few dollars.

Oh, and you'll undoubtedly need access to an actual kitchen sink. But you probably guessed that already.

# SETTING UP

The key to any successful experiment is preparation. Here's how we recommend you get set up in your very own Institute of Kitchen Science.

First and foremost, before you start an experiment, you should read the instructions through once, make sure you have all the ingredients on hand, and note any potential safety issues before you start. We understand that not everyone enjoys following instructions, but we promise that doing so will save you time in the long run and ensure that you're able to complete the experiment successfully—rather than having to give up because of some unforeseen complication.

Second, because many experiments involve steps that are time-sensitive, we suggest you assemble everything in the YOU WILL NEED list before you start, so there aren't any delays.

Third, make sure your kitchen lab is well ventilated and well lit. Although none of the experiments in this book produce anything noxious, you're going to be working with some strong-smelling materials and liquids, so ventilation is a must. Similarly, you need to be able to see what you're doing!

Fourth, your home situation may make it inconvenient for others if you take over the kitchen for the afternoon, so plan ahead and get clearance from the rest of your family and/or roommates. Let's face it, they may not be as intrigued as you to see a circle of flaming teabag ascending into the air while they're just trying to enjoy a bowl of cornflakes (which you may need to borrow for the experiment on pages 150–153).

Fifth, gather as you go. If you're taking the scientific life seriously, it might be a good idea to set aside a corner of the kitchen for basic lab-related supplies—washed and empty plastic bottles, for example, or items you only use occasionally in everyday life (such as rubber bands, Styrofoam™ plates and bowls, very large plastic bottles and so on)—so that you don't have to acquire them especially when the time comes to start experimenting.

A happy kitchen is an organized kitchen, so with any luck you'll already know where most of your essential equipment and ingredients are stored. If not, then take this as an opportunity to inject some order into your kitchen and get things squared away so you can find them easily when assembling the YOU WILL NEED list.

Sixth, many of the experiments use approximate measurements—½ cup, for example—but we've found that one of the most useful items in any home experimentation kit is a proper measuring spoon: the kind that's actually four or five spoons attached to a keyring. These also have the benefit of being easy to clean.

And finally, clean as you go to make sure the next experiment isn't contaminated by the ingredients from the previous one.

Throughout this book you'll see that we refer to "your kitchen table" as a sort of HQ for experimentation. This is simply because a kitchen table is likely to be functional rather than decorative, and thus able to withstand the chemical slings and arrows you're going to throw at it. If, however, you're concerned about your kitchen table's wellbeing (not to mention copious amounts of vinegar) you can do these experiments on a countertop or other work surface. Alternatively, just add this sentence to the start of every experiment: "Having covered your kitchen table with old newspaper to protect it…" and you'll be just fine.

## LABORATORY ASSISTANTS

We've tried to make the experiments simple enough so that you can do almost all of them unassisted. There are times when you'll clearly need more than one person—either because you're a human and not an octopus, or because you're a youngster and you should have an adult on hand—but most are designed to be done solo.

## PART 1

# MYSTERIOUS MOTION

# CONTENTS

# PING-PONG JET STREAM

## Explore the principles of flight

**Make sure the inlet of the hairdryer isn't resting on a carpet or any flammable soft furnishings.**

## SETUP

Set the hairdryer to blow cool air only and point it up at the ceiling. You can hold it or wedge it carefully between some books or other heavy objects. Make sure it's steady and then, carefully, pop a ping-pong ball into the air stream and watch what happens.

Although gravity is trying to pull the ping-pong ball down, the pressure from the air coming out of the hairdryer keeps it suspended. These forces are said to be balanced. There's something else at work here too: the Coanda Effect (named after its discoverer, the aerodynamics pioneer Henri Coanda). This describes what happens when a fluid (in this case, air) moves over a circular object and presses evenly on it from all sides, creating a capsule, or pocket, in which the ball floats. This effect is powerful enough that you can tilt the hair dryer slightly and the ball will still float.

The ping-pong ball will shoot up and out of the toilet paper tube because, once it is inside, the surrounding air pressure effectively disappears, so the only real force being exerted on the ball is coming from the dryer.

## TESTING

When switched on, the air coming out of the hairdryer is moving much faster than the surrounding air, and so it is able to keep the ball suspended. In fact, the air flow is so strong that you can even angle the hairdryer to almost 45 degrees and the ball will continue to float quite happily.

You can try adding a second, or even a third, ball to see how they behave, and you can also try putting the empty toilet paper tube over a single floating ball to see what happens—but stand back! What happens if you try placing a balloon in the air stream?

## PUZZLER!?!

Interestingly, a balloon won't float in the stream at all. What do you think you could do to make the balloon float successfully?

# FLYING TEABAGS

## Watch as teabags become fire lanterns

**YOU WILL NEED:**
• Teabags (the kind that have a little label attached with string)
• Tinfoil • Scissors • Matches
OPTIONAL:
• Empty toilet paper roll
• Tissue paper • Glue

You don't have to use tinfoil; you can use any non-combustible material—a china saucer, for example, or if you want to use multiple teabags, a large plate.

## SETUP

It's important that you use the right kind of teabags—you *have* to use the ones that have a label attached with a bit of string, because these open up to form a nice cylinder. Take a teabag and cut the top off where the string and label are attached. Open the bag carefully and pour out the tea. You'll be left with a tube or cylinder made of teabag material. Stand this upright on a piece of tinfoil. Light the top of the teabag cylinder with a match and watch what happens.

1

2

3

4

## TESTING

When you light the top of the teabag it begins to smolder. Because the paper the teabags are made out of is porous and light, it will burn in just a few moments. At first, the bag just burns where it is sitting, but as the flames consume the cylinder and reach the bottom, the bag—or what's left of it—is pulled off the tinfoil and then rises quickly into the air. As the fire turns the paper into ash, the flames are extinguished and the residue floats back down to earth.

You can try arranging several teabag cylinders in a line or in other shapes, such as a circle, and then lighting them in quick succession. This will create interesting three-dimensional patterns as the burning bags rise into the air one after another.

## ADDITIONAL SETUP

If you'd like to discover whether the size, shape, or material of the cylinder makes a difference to what happens, you can experiment further. You might use an empty toilet paper roll, which has the same shape as the teabag tube and will also burn. What happens when you light that?

Or you could create a larger "teabag" from tissue paper. Just roll it into a cylinder shape and then secure it with glue. What happens when you light the top of the tissue? Does it fly in the same way as the smaller teabag?

Flying teabags are really light so, if possible, you should perform this experiment in a room with the windows closed. If there's a draft or a breeze they'll be blown all over the place.

# IN CONCLUSION

Warm air rises; for example, on a hot day you'll notice that it's always warmer upstairs than it is on the first floor of a building. The same principle is at work here. When you light the top of the teabag, it heats up the air inside the cylinder. This agitates the air molecules, making them move around much faster, and they spread out to take up more of the available space. As the air molecules move further apart, this has the effect of making the air less dense. The result? The hot, less dense air rises above the surrounding denser, colder air. The flame turns the teabag to ash, which is so light that the hotter, less dense air inside is able to generate enough lift to make what's left of the teabag float up into the air. The relative weight of the cardboard in the toilet paper tube is the reason it doesn't fly at all, but just burns in place. The amount of lift simply isn't great enough to counteract gravity.

This is the same principle that's used in hot-air balloons. Joseph-Michel Montgolfier and his brother, Jacques-Etienne, are credited with achieving the first hot-air balloon flight in 1783. Unsure of the safety of their invention, the brothers popped a duck, a cockerel, and a sheep into the attached basket and were delighted when it flew for eight minutes and traveled a distance of 2 miles (3km). The villagers who watched it land were less delighted, however: scared out of their wits, they promptly attacked it.

These days, hot-air balloons are popular for sightseeing and are especially suitable for activities such as animal safaris, as their relative silence means they don't spook sensitive wildlife.

## PUZZLER!?!

How much further does a cylinder of tissue paper fly and why?

# #3
# THE DANCING COIN

## Money doesn't just talk—it's also got moves!

**YOU WILL NEED:**
- Bowl of ice water
- Glass soda bottle
- Coin slightly bigger than the bottle opening

Bottle too cold for your hands? The trick will work if you wear a pair of wool gloves, but you'll need to hold the bottle for longer.

## SETUP

Drop the coin into the bowl of ice water, then upturn the bottle and hold it with the top face-down in the water, so it gets good and cold. Wait 10 minutes then take the coin and the bottle out. Turn the bottle right side up, place it on the kitchen table or countertop, and place the coin over the opening. Wrap both your hands around the bottle and carefully watch the coin.

# TESTING

When you wrap both of your warm hands around the icy bottle and leave them there for a minute or so, the coin will judder and then actually lift up from the top of the bottle. Leave your hands there a bit longer and it'll happen again. Take your hands away and it'll still happen once or twice more. The coin appears to be "dancing."

# IN CONCLUSION

This experiment is all to do with thermal expansion. After being dunked in the ice bath, the bottle, the air inside it, and the coin are all very cold, so when you sit the coin on top of the bottle, nothing happens. However, when you wrap warm hands around the bottle, you heat the air molecules inside, which expand and start looking for a way out. The pressure isn't strong enough to break the glass of course, but it is strong enough to push the edge of the coin up. And so the dance begins.

Thermal expansion is great for fitting stuff together snugly. For example, if component A is slightly smaller than component B but needs to fit over it, you might heat component A until it expands, then fit the part, and wait for it to contract back to its "normal" size. This is called a "shrink fit."

# THE MATCHSTICK ROCKET

## A mini missile that packs a helluva punch

**YOU WILL NEED:**
- Big box of matches
- 6in (15cm) wooden skewer
- Scissors • Tinfoil • Hole punch
- Small candle/tea light

OPTIONAL:
- Glue

!

If you're going to do this in your kitchen, make sure you have a nice open area with nothing nearby that can be damaged by the flaming match. And always point the rocket away from you.

# SETUP

Cut the head off a match. Cut a 2 × 4in (5 × 10cm) rectangle of tinfoil and lay the skewer on top of it, parallel to the shorter side. Lay the match head on top of the skewer and arrange both so that there's about ½ in of foil above the match head. Roll the match head and skewer up in the foil, then very firmly crimp the end above the match head and tightly twist it round. Remove the skewer. Empty the matchbox and punch a hole in the lid, close to the short edge. Slide the lid back onto the match box and poke the skewer through the hole at an angle. Slide the foil rocket onto the end, pointing away from you. Light a small candle underneath the rocket's "nose" and stand back. Don't be tempted to pick up your rocket... just wait.

# THE MATCHSTICK ROCKET

## TESTING

So, what happened?

If you've used a decent match, wrapped it well and crimped the top properly, your missile should shoot off the end of the skewer at breakneck speed. If it didn't, try repeating the process again.

If you're still disappointed at the distance your rocket is achieving, experiment with using different kinds of matches to see whether the result varies or not. You should resist the temptation to pile a load of match heads into the foil, though, because you're trying to make a rocket—not a bomb! For the same reason, we'd also suggest that you should avoid using one of those

camping matches that have an ultra-long head and are designed to stay alight in the rain.

You may be tempted to use either another match or a lighter to start your rocket—don't. A match probably won't burn for long enough to heat the match head inside the foil and using a lighter will mean holding your hand too close to the rocket.

Once you've got the setup right, you could also try altering the angle of the skewer to see if you can get the rocket to fly higher and/or further.

# ADDITIONAL SETUP

You can also try adding some tail fins to your rocket. Cut a 1 × 1in (2.5 × 2.5cm) square of tinfoil and fold it diagonally twice to make a little triangle. Holding it by the longest edge, find the corner on the opposite side and cut off a tiny piece (see the diagram below). Open out the foil and you should have a small hole in the center. Squish the foil around the hole, then poke the bottom of the rocket into the hole and glue it in place. Shape the foil into four tail fins. Set the rocket aside to dry and then try launching it again.

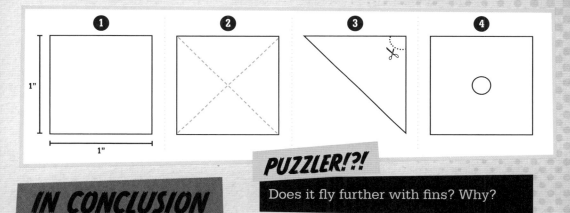

## PUZZLER!?!

Does it fly further with fins? Why?

# IN CONCLUSION

Congratulations! You've built a rocket. The aluminum foil, crimped at the nose but hollow and open at the end, acts as a combustion chamber so that when the match head finally ignites, it creates lots of gas—made up of tiny particles—which looks for a way out. Because the exit is so small, this creates additional pressure inside the chamber, which in turn creates thrust, or the movement of mass in a single direction. This action produces a force in the opposite direction—the reaction—which propels the rocket across the kitchen. This is an example of Isaac Newton's third law of motion: For every action there is an equal and opposite reaction.

Rocketry like this has been the mainstay of space exploration since the Soviet cosmonaut Yuri Gagarin first orbited the Earth in 1961. It was the technology that put the first astronauts on the moon and, until something better comes along, it's likely to put people on Mars and maybe beyond.

# THIS CANDLE SUCKS

## It does... it really does

## SETUP

Pour about ½in (1cm) of water into the dish and mix in a couple of drops of food coloring. Place the candle in the middle of the dish and light it with the match. Place the glass upside-down over the candle. Now sit back and await the results.

Instinctively, this feels like a simple experiment but, in fact, it's more complex because there are two related things going on. First, as the air molecules inside the glass heat up, they expand, increasing the pressure. When the candle goes out, the molecules cool and the pressure drops again, so that it's less than the air pressure outside the glass. Because pressure always wants to equalize, the higher air pressure outside "pushes" the water up and into the glass where the pressure is lower. It may do this with such force that the water actually bubbles.

At the same time, because twice as much oxygen is burned as carbon dioxide released during combustion, the gas volume decreases. This also has the effect of reducing the overall pressure inside the glass, causing the water to be sucked into it.

## TESTING

While the candle is burning, it doesn't look like there's much going on. However, as soon as the candle starts to go out, the water in the bowl is sucked into the glass and may even begin to bubble. Once the candle is fully extinguished, the water stays in the glass until you lift it up, at which point it pours back out into the bowl. Try experimenting with different candle and glass sizes to see if they make a difference to the experiment. What do you think the optimum combination will be?

We found that this experiment works best with a tea light—a little candle with a metal casing—and a tall glass. The water is sucked in with such force that the candle floats!

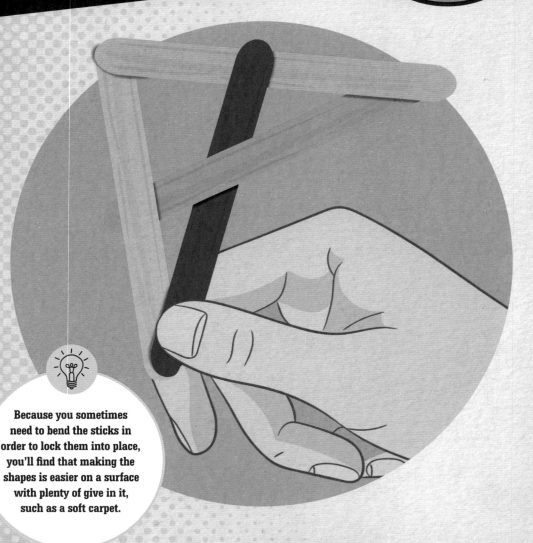

# NINJA STICKS

## (Not quite) deadly throwing sticks that explode on impact

**YOU WILL NEED:**
- A bunch of wooden craft sticks (the more you have the more ninja sticks you can make)
- Protective eyewear such as an old pair of glasses

Because you sometimes need to bend the sticks in order to lock them into place, you'll find that making the shapes is easier on a surface with plenty of give in it, such as a soft carpet.

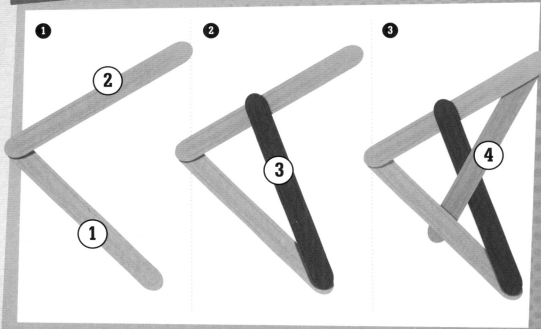

We'll start with the simplest design, which is made up of four craft sticks. Here's how to set it up. Take the first two sticks and place the tip of stick 2 over the tip of stick 1 and arrange them to make an arrowhead. Take stick 3 and place its tip over the tip at the other end of stick 1 and lay the other end over the middle of stick 2. With us so far? Now, press down with the thumb and first finger of one hand on the point where sticks 1 and 2 meet and the end where sticks 1 and 3 meet—this will cause one end of stick 3 to rise slightly. You can now add stick 4 so one end goes under the middle of stick 1, the middle goes over the middle of stick 3 and under the end of stick 2. Phew!

## TESTING

If you built the ninja stick correctly, it'll feel pretty sturdy. You'll be able to hold it by any end and wave it about vigorously without worrying that it'll fall apart. Now try throwing it against the wall or lobbing it onto a hard surface and watch what happens. Suddenly, that solid structure doesn't seem quite so solid anymore, does it?

# NINJA STICKS

## ADDITIONAL SETUP

Let's try another shape, this time made up of five craft sticks arranged as follows. Take sticks 1 and 2 and make them into a cross. Then, lay stick 3 over the top of them to make a six-pointed star shape. Now, press down on the middle of the arrangement (the center, where the three sticks meet). Then place stick 4 over one end of stick 3, and under the ends of sticks 1 and 2. Now, press down on the ends of the stick you just added and weave stick 5 into the other side using the same under-over-under arrangement. The shape—sometimes called a "butterfly ninja"—is now locked in place and ready to be thrown.

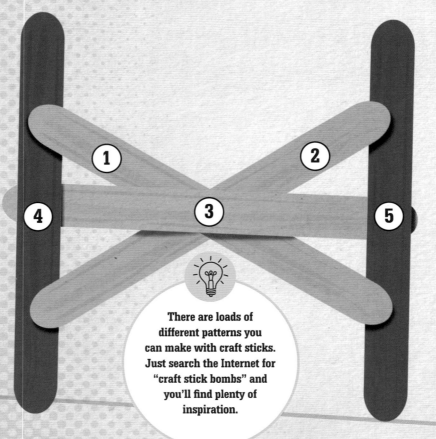

There are loads of different patterns you can make with craft sticks. Just search the Internet for "craft stick bombs" and you'll find plenty of inspiration.

## ADDITIONAL SETUP (EXPERT MODE)

Now you're a pro, it's time to introduce you to the infamous "cobra weave." We're not going to try and explain how to make this; instead, copy the pattern in the illustration above. You can make the cobra weave as long as you like, but you should try it with at least 30. When you get to the end, secure it by placing a last stick as shown by the vertical orange stick in the illustration. When it's finished, go back to the beginning and remove the very first stick from the cobra weave and watch what happens.

## IN CONCLUSION

Something that is structurally straight but slightly flexible—like a wooden craft stick—will always try to return to its resting state. So, when you bend it over or under another craft stick, you create tension, which in turn creates potential or stored energy. Every single one of the sticks in whichever pattern you make wants to be straight—it's straining to be straight. So, when you release the tension, either by throwing your sticks against a hard surface or by releasing a stick that's holding others in place, you release that tension, and that potential energy is transformed into kinetic energy. That's why the sticks either blow apart or, in the case of the cobra weave, create a wonderful, rolling wave effect.

The cobra weave is also a great example of a chain reaction, where one thing happens as a consequence of something else, which happens as a consequence of something else… and so on.

# 7

# DOUBLE CUP FLYER

## This peculiar plane flies remarkably far

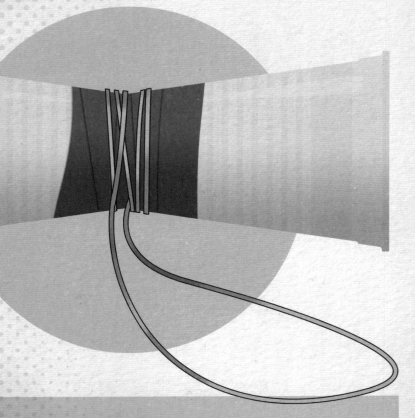

## SETUP

Place the two cups bottom-to-bottom and tape them together very firmly. Loop the rubber bands together to make one long one. With the thumb of one hand, hold one end of the rubber band against the middle of the join between the cups and, with the other, wrap the elastic around the center join counterclockwise until you have a couple of inches left that you can hold with the other hand. Using the elastic like a slingshot, you can now catapult your "plane" into the air.

## TESTING

It may take a few goes to get this right. You're trying to set the two cups spinning counterclockwise, very fast. The best motion is to hold the cups near your body with one hand and pull the elastic band with the other hand out in front of you. Then, when you release the cup, move your front hand down at the same time as if you were starting a race with a flag—if you don't, the cups may simply bang into your hand. You can also try winding the elastic around the cups clockwise. What happens to the plane then?

## IN CONCLUSION

This peculiar plane doesn't look like it should go anywhere. It flouts all the laws of aerodynamics. It's not sleek, and it doesn't have any fins to stabilize it or wings to let it ride air currents. It's just two cups stuck together.

The secret is something called the Magnus effect, named after Heinrich Gustav Magnus, who discovered it in 1852 when he was trying to work out why cannonballs didn't fly straight. As the "plane" spins at speed it creates a kind of whirlpool of air around itself and—being ultralight—the plane is buffeted along by this air pocket, and floats on it.

If you've ever watched baseball, cricket, or tennis, you'll have seen the Magnus effect in action. A bowler will put backspin on a ball to make it travel further, a tennis player will hit a ball with topspin so it curves down unexpectedly.

# 8

# THE LIGHT THAT ROCKS THE CANDLE

## Just light it up and watch it go...

**YOU WILL NEED:**
- Two identical glasses
- Thin candle • Knife
- Pen • Matches • Long darning needle • Sheet of newspaper

OPTIONAL:
- Ruler

## SETUP

Carefully cut partway through the bottom of the candle until you can pull the wax away to reveal the wick. Find the balancing point of the candle by placing it horizontally on your finger and mark the point with a pen. (Alternatively, you can measure your candle from end to end to find its middle.) Heat the end of the needle with a match, and then holding the candle steady by the sides, carefully push the needle through the center at the balancing point. Lay the sheet of newspaper down, pop the glasses on top, and then balance the candle between them, with the needle resting on the glasses. Light both ends of the candle and watch what happens.

## TESTING

Once it has started to rock, the candle will continue to seesaw unattended for some time—the larger the candle, the longer it will keep going. If you're finding it hard to balance the candle between the glasses, light the lower wick first and then wait for that end to come up before lighting the other end. You can also give it a little nudge to get it rocking if you need to.

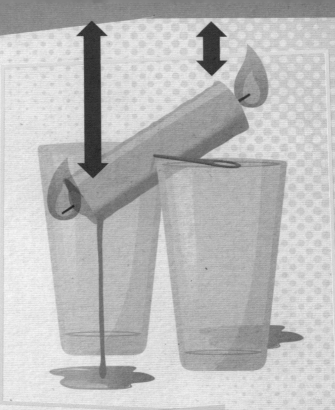

## PUZZLER!?!

Which of Newton's laws of motion applies here?

## IN CONCLUSION

When balanced, the unlit candle achieves equilibrium and doesn't move. By lighting the ends you set the seesawing motion in action. As one end drips wax, it becomes lighter and rises, and the other end falls. This exposes more of the wax to the flame on that end. It begins to melt more quickly, loses more mass than the other end, and so rises. Then the process starts all over again. At the same time, potential energy stored in the candle is turned into kinetic energy—the heat from the candle flame.

This is also a lever, one of the six "simple machines" that form the basis of many more complex ones. (The other five are the wheel and axle, inclined plane, wedge, pulley, and screw.) The Greek philosopher Archimedes studied levers around 250 BCE, but it wasn't until the Renaissance in the 15th century that the simple machines began to be studied together as a group.

# 9

# WRITING'S WRONG

## What's in control—
## your hand or your foot?

## SETUP

Sit comfortably on the chair, raise your right leg into the air slightly, and then begin to make clockwise circles with your foot. At the same time, raise your right arm and draw the number "6" in the air in front of you. How did you get on?

## TESTING

It's a mess, isn't it? As soon as you start to try to draw the "6" in the air, your arm probably goes berserk, making weird shapes in front of you and doing everything *but* drawing that wretched number. If this doesn't happen and you're actually able to draw the "6," notice that your right foot isn't moving in neat clockwise circles anymore but has started to waggle about all over the place.

Now stop. Take a break. Then try again, but this time, use your right foot and your left hand. How did you do this time?

As a variation, rotate your foot as before but try writing your name on a piece of paper instead of drawing the "6" in the air.

## IN CONCLUSION

Most people know that the left hemisphere of the brain controls the right side of the body and the right side looks after the left side of the body. However, there's more to it than that. The left side of our brain also takes care of rhythm and timing, and it can't cope with two wildly different—in this case, opposite—movements at the same time, so in an attempt to circle the foot and draw a "6" simultaneously, it mashes them together. Hence your arm and leg end up just sort of flailing about. When you switch arms, however, everything goes back to normal because both hemispheres of the brain are engaged and are able to operate independently from each other.

It was previously thought that most of us have one hemisphere of the brain that is dominant. However, recent research using new imaging technology shows that the two hemispheres are highly complementary, with both the left and right sides of the brain working together to perform a broad range of tasks.

# 10

# FOLLOW THE LIGHT

## Want a plant that grows around corners? No problem!

**YOU WILL NEED:**
- Empty shoebox
- Two extra pieces of cardboard the same height as the shoebox • Sticky tape
- Scissors • A climbing plant (almost any sort will work) in a little pot with soil

Make sure you give the plant plenty of water before you seal it into the box.

## SETUP

Open the shoebox. Measure and cut two pieces of cardboard that are the same height as the shoebox but only two-thirds its width. Use the tape to stick them to the inside of the box in the staggered arrangement that's shown in the illustration opposite. Then use the scissors to make a hole about 1in (2.5cm) wide and 3in (7.6cm) long at one end of the shoebox. Place the shoebox on its end with the hole pointing up, put the plant pot at the bottom (under the first bit of cardboard), and then slide the lid back on and tape it shut.

## IN CONCLUSION

The stems of plants contain hormones called auxins that control the speed at which the plants grow. Sunlight burns these hormones away so the side of the plant that's closest to the light grows more slowly, while the side furthest away from the light grows faster. This has the effect of making the plant in your shoebox grow toward the light—and around corners! This tendency to grow toward light, so that photosynthesis can take place, is called phototropism.

The scientific author Sir Thomas Browne is thought to have conducted the first experiment to demonstrate phototropism in 1658, when he observed that a mustard plant would always turn toward the sun, even when he rotated its pot.

## TESTING

Place the shoebox with the hole facing up in a sunny spot, such as on a windowsill in your kitchen. Leave it for four or five days and then, carefully, unseal the box and take a peek at what's happened inside. You'll discover that the plant has negotiated a path around the two bits of cardboard (your mini maze) and is making its way toward the light.

# PART 2

# FANTASTIC FORCES

# CONTENTS

# SODA CAN CRUSHER

## Can air really crush a can? This can can!

## SETUP

Take your empty soda can and pour in a little bit of water—about an inch (2.5cm) usually does the trick. Next, take a shallow bowl and fill it with ice-cold water. Sit the can on a hot plate or a metal dish on your stovetop (or a camping stove), and keep an eye on it while the can heats up. You want to be able to see some steam coming out of the top of the can, but you don't want to let it boil dry. Once you see the steam, wait about 30 seconds, then you're ready to start crushing.

**You absolutely must use tongs to pick up the can.**

## TESTING

Pick up the can with the tongs and then, very quickly, turn it over (so the open slot is facing down) and plunge it into the bowl of ice-cold water. What do you think will happen? (Of course, the title gives it away, but were you really expecting such a violent transformation?)

Now see what happens if you take the crumpled can out of the bowl.

## IN CONCLUSION

When you plunge the hot can into the cold water it implodes. This is the opposite of an explosion: instead of matter and energy flying outward in all directions, they collapse inward, but with just as much force.

When you place the hot can into the icy water, it cools rapidly. The water and water vapor inside the can condense incredibly quickly, reducing down into a couple of drops of water. This water takes up less space, which causes the pressure inside the can to drop. The result? The huge difference in air pressure inside and outside the can creates a mighty inward force that crumples the can as if it has been crushed by the hand of an invisible giant.

Water pours out of the can when you pick it up because the force of the implosion is so strong that it sucks water from the bowl up into the can.

# THE NOT-SO-STATIC SNAKE

## Charming a paper snake turns out to be sssssiimple...

## SETUP

Draw out a spiral on your piece of tissue paper—about three "turns" should be enough—and then cut along the spiral with your scissors. Shape the head of the snake with the scissors, then color it in and decorate it with stripes, eyes, and nostrils. Rub the plastic ruler on the wool item and then hold it over the head of the snake. What do you think is going to happen and why?

While this experiment is perfectly safe, if you over-charge your ruler or pen you may get a tiny shock of static electricity.

## TESTING

As you hold the ruler over the head of your snake, it'll rise up into the air as if by magic. Once you've tried that, replace the ruler with the hollow tube from a ballpoint pen—except this time after rubbing the plastic tube hold it in your mouth like a snake charmer's whistle. While the ruler should only take about 30 seconds to charge, if you move on to try the plastic pen, you'll need some patience because it will take longer to generate the required charge. This is because the ruler has a greater surface area, so it absorbs the charge more quickly.

## IN CONCLUSION

Static is a kind of electricity that can be caused by friction, or the rubbing together of two surfaces that aren't good electrical conductors. Normally, positive and negative electrical charges are balanced and an object is said to be neutral—that's why most of the time we can walk around touching stuff without getting a shock. However, friction produces an imbalance between the negative and positive charges, and this sits on the surface until it can be released—either by touching or coming close to another object. When the plastic ruler is rubbed against the wool, it gains a static charge. The tissue paper is attracted to the charge and, because the paper is so light, the snake rises into the air as if charmed.

Who discovered static electricity? We think it was the ancient Greeks who first stumbled upon it around 600 BCE while polishing stones made of amber (fossilized tree resin) with fur to make them shine. They noticed that after vigorous rubbing the hairs on the fur rose up whenever they brought the amber near them.

# #13 ⚠ VACUUM-PACKED TEDDY

## It's a teddy bear, in a bag, and it can't move!

> ! OK, you know this and we know this, but it's worth saying again: any experiment—even one as fun and daft as this—involving plastic bags needs to be handled responsibly. Never, ever, put the bag over someone's head—not even teddy's.

## SETUP

Start by explaining to your bear in a friendly fashion that they've been taking up too much space recently and you need to pack them down a bit smaller. Now, examine the plastic bag for holes. If you find any (apart from the opening at the top) discard the bag and use a fresh one. We found that a lightweight, general-purpose plastic bag works better than a heavy-duty sack.

Place your teddy bear into the bag and pull it up around their shoulders. Adjust their legs so they're sitting on the floor. Wrap the top of the bag around so there are no gaps around their shoulders. Feed in the hose from the vacuum cleaner and maneuver the nozzle in such a way that the end doesn't touch the bear or the bag. Use your other hand to make the seal at the top of the bag as airtight as you can. (It'll never be completely airtight but do your best.) Ready? Turn on the vacuum cleaner.

## TESTING

As soon as you turn on the vacuum cleaner it will start to suck air out of the bag. Very quickly, the sides of the bag will be sucked in and cling to the shape of the bear's legs, arms, and body. Any available space inside the bag will disappear and, should your bear choose this moment to miraculously come to life, they'll find it very difficult—if not impossible—to move. They're vacuum-packed!

Check your bear for any sharp "extras" like claws badges, brooches, and so on. This is to make sure they don't poke a hole in the bag by accident.

# VACUUM-PACKED TEDDY

## ADDITIONAL SETUP

You can also use this technique for something that's actually useful: packing clothes away for winter storage inside a garbage bag. Check the bag for holes, then fill it two-thirds full with folded clothes. Gather up the remaining third of the bag to form a "neck," and poke the nozzle of the vacuum cleaner into it. Use your hand to make a seal around the nozzle. Turn on the vacuum cleaner and wait for it to suck all the air out of the bag. When that's happened, turn the vacuum off and, in one smooth movement, remove the nozzle with one hand while twisting the neck of the bag closed with the other. Secure it with tape, and you're done!

## IN CONCLUSION

The atmospheric pressure at sea level is 14.7lbs per square inch (about 10 tons per square meter), or the equivalent of having a Toyota Yaris (a small super-mini) strapped to the top of your head. The reason we're not all crawling around on our hands and knees is because all the air inside us—in our lungs, stomach, and everywhere else—is exerting the same pressure outward, so the two cancel each other out.

It's the same deal with the air outside the bag and the air inside the bag. But when you use the vacuum cleaner to suck air out of the bag, you're creating lower pressure inside it—using a standard household vacuum cleaner you can reduce it by between 5 and 20 percent. The greater air pressure outside the bag pushes the plastic in toward the lower air pressure areas inside, and it keeps going because even when it comes into contact with the bear's arms, legs, and body, there are all sorts of little folds that it can push into. In addition, because plastic is so flexible, the bag stretches and will continue to press against vac-packed Ted, making it even more difficult for them to move.

Vacuum packing is used extensively in everyday life, whether it's for packing winter clothes and bedding away into storage so they take up less space, for squeezing more into your luggage for a summer vacation, or keeping food fresh (where there's no air, there's no bacteria, so food doesn't break down and will stay fresh longer).

Once you've done
this with one bear,
they're all going to want
to have a go, the second your
back is turned. Just remind them
what happened last time (you
know, with the honey jar) and
make sure they don't try it
without supervision.

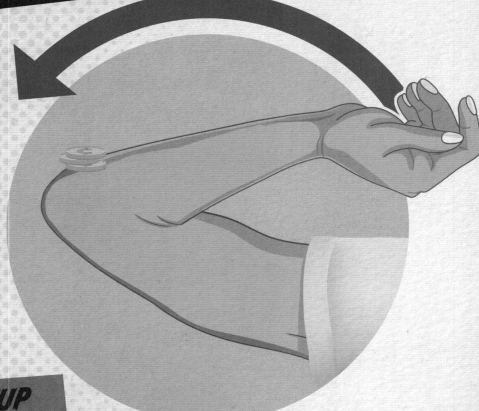

# 14

# COIN SNATCHER

## Can you make a coin defy gravity?

**YOU WILL NEED:**
- One or more coins of the same size
- An elbow (preferably your own)

## SETUP

Select your favorite arm (alright, the one that you use most) and roll your sleeve up so it's bare. Then bend your arm back so your elbow is pointing out in front of you and your palm is facing up. Place a single coin on the flat part of your forearm near your elbow. Then, in one smooth motion, flip your arm forward as if you were throwing a ball. Can you catch the coin?

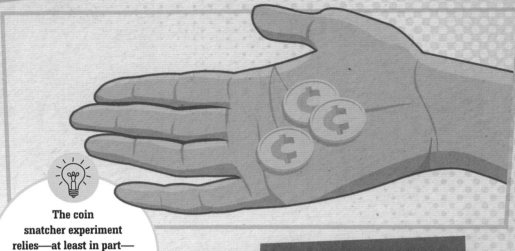

The coin snatcher experiment relies—at least in part—on that most unscientific of phenomena, the "knack." You have to keep going until you get it.

## TESTING

This experiment requires practice. At first, it may appear frustratingly impossible to catch the coin and then suddenly, once you've lost count of your attempts, it'll happen. After that it will become easier and easier. You can then experiment by adding a second coin, then a third, and so on. As your confidence grows, you could try using both arms at the same time. You could even attempt the infamous crossover move, where you catch coins resting on your right elbow with your left hand, and those on your left elbow with the right hand. If you think that sounds tough, consider that the world record is 328 UK 10-pence coins. Yep, 328!

## IN CONCLUSION

Despite our joke about the "knack," there's also a sound scientific principle behind this experiment: inertia. This is the propensity of an object to carry on doing whatever it's doing until it meets enough external force to start it, if it's not moving, or, if it is moving, to stop it or make it change direction.

To start with, the coins are motionless, sitting on your elbow. When you move your arm, the coins seem to hang momentarily in the air, as inertia means that they start to fall extremely slowly. That gives your arm—which is moving fast—time to catch up with and grab the coins before they tumble to the floor.

This technique is also known as "cobra coin catching" because the action of the arm mimics that of a striking snake.

# 15

# THE UNPOPPABLE BALLOON

Fire + balloon doesn't always = POP!

## SETUP

First, blow up the balloon as normal and then tie the end. Light the candle and then slowly lower the balloon over the flame. How close can you get before the inevitable happens and the balloon pops?

Now take another balloon, stretch it over the faucet of your kitchen sink, and fill it with cold water. When the uninflated balloon is full of water, blow it up as before and tie the end so you've got an inflated balloon with a pool of water inside covering the bottom. Now take the candle and place it in the middle of the washing-up bowl. Light the candle and slowly lower the balloon toward the flame again. How close can you get to the flame this time, and what happens when you do?

## TESTING

When you hold the balloon containing cold water over the candle, you'd expect the balloon to pop and for water to go everywhere (hence the washing-up bowl) but, instead, something more surprising happens: the rubber doesn't melt and the balloon doesn't burst. You can even touch the surface of the balloon to the flame and it still won't burst—though it will make a sooty mark on the surface of the balloon, which is actually a deposit of carbon. When the balloon is filled with air rather than cold water, however, it pops almost immediately.

Try seeing how long you can hold the balloon with the water in it over the candle before it bursts.

## IN CONCLUSION

This works because of the different conductivity properties of air and water. Water is a much better conductor and is able to absorb the heat from the candle and dissipate it. As the water at the bottom of the balloon heats up, it rises to the surface and is replaced by colder water. Importantly, this happens at a rate faster than the rate at which the rubber perishes, which is why the balloon with water in the bottom doesn't burst—well, it will eventually, but not for quite a while. When the balloon is filled just with air, there's nothing to absorb the heat from the candle and the rubber gets very hot and perishes... hence the pop.

# 16

# THE ATTRACTIVE PENCIL

## What can you attract with a pencil?

**YOU WILL NEED:**
- Small plastic jar or bottle
- Uncooked rice • Pencil

OPTIONAL:
- 20fl oz (60cl) plastic bottle

## SETUP

Take the plastic jar and almost fill it with the uncooked rice—about four-fifths full will be just perfect. Place the filled jar on your kitchen table and poke the pencil into the rice until the point touches the bottom of the jar. Very carefully, try and lift the jar of rice with the pencil. Unsurprisingly, it'll pull straight out. Is there any way to use the pencil to lift the jar like this?

It takes a few goes to get this right. We found that short, sharp stabs work best.

## TESTING

This time, poke the pencil into the rice and then pull it back out. Then do it again. Keep doing it—in and out, in and out, about 40 times, as if you hate the rice and want to stab it. After the 40th time, leave the pencil in there. Then hold the end of the pencil and very carefully lift it, as if you're pulling it out of the jar. What do you think is going to happen?

Try changing the type of container. What happens, for example, when you use a 20fl oz (60cl) plastic bottle filled with rice? Is it possible to achieve the lift with fewer stabs?

## IN CONCLUSION

It's all to do with friction, or the action of one object rubbing against another. A single push of the pencil doesn't produce enough friction, but when you keep pushing and pulling the pencil in and out of the rice you compact it, pushing the rice together and forcing air out. Eventually this compaction generates enough friction to overcome gravity and you can lift the jar of rice up into the air.

Using a taller receptacle may allow you to achieve the same result with fewer stabs because the friction between the rice and the pencil is distributed over a greater surface area.

Although often seen as a negative phenomenon, without friction, many day-to-day activities would be impossible. Walking, for example, or writing a shopping list, even riding a bicycle.

# 17

# THE FLOATING ARM TRICK

## This classic kid's party trick works on adults too

When you step out of the doorway, you must relax your arms as much as possible so they can do their thing.

## SETUP

Stand in an open doorway with your arms held loosely at your sides and both palms facing inward. Now raise both arms so they're pressing against the doorframe. Push outward as hard as you can for a minimum of 30 seconds—a bit longer is even better. Then step forward, out of the doorway, and relax your arms.

## TESTING

If you've followed the setup instructions, then, as you step forward into the room and relax your arms, they will rise into the air—without any effort on your part—until your whole body forms a nice "T" shape.

Your first challenge here is to keep a straight face when the inevitable happens. This is tougher than it sounds because the temptation is to break out into a large grin.

Your second challenge is to prevent your arms from rising into the air. This is actually very simple to do: just think about keeping them at your sides and you'll discover that when you concentrate, the muscular impulse is quite easy to resist.

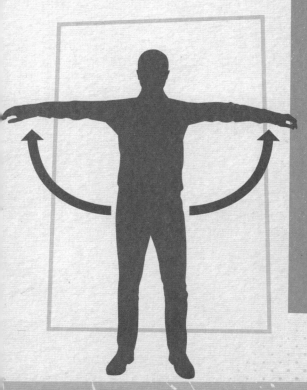

## IN CONCLUSION

When you push against the doorframe, your muscles contract and hold one position. This is sometimes known as static strength, as opposed to dynamic strength (when muscles contract and extend) or explosive strength (when the contraction happens at speed).

Your muscles contract when you push against the frame but the doorway prevents your arms from going anywhere. Nerve endings don't understand this and so keep sending messages to your arms to try harder. When you step away from the doorway, this pent-up energy is released and your arms rise into the air.

What you've experienced here is known as Kohnstamm's phenomenon, named after the German neurologist Oskar Kohnstamm, who first observed it in 1915.

Understanding the way the brain controls this kind of muscle contraction may have life-changing applications in treating conditions where patients have problems with involuntary movement, such as Parkinson's disease.

# BALANCING ACT

## It's not magic—it's science!

**YOU WILL NEED:**
- Heavy drinking glass
- Metal fork with four tines • Metal spoon (e.g. a tablespoon) about the same length and weight as the fork • Toothpicks
- Matches

Having trouble balancing your fork and spoon? As we say in the setup, it's helpful if they're more or less the same size and weight. Try changing one or both and see if that improves things.

Place the fork on the kitchen table as if you were setting a place for dinner and, holding the handle down, bend the two middle tines upward slightly. Now pick up the fork and turn it over. Take the spoon and, holding it with the bowl facing down, gently—but firmly—push it in between the end tines of the fork. You'll know you've done it properly when you can hold both utensils by either end, wave them about a bit, and they don't come apart. Next, poke one of the toothpicks between the second and third tines of the fork so it rests against the head of the spoon. You want to push one end through just far enough so you can sit the other end on the tip of your finger. Once you've got that right, you should be able to balance the fork and spoon perfectly on your fingertip.

## TESTING

Once you've successfully balanced the fork and spoon, there's not really very much else to test. This is one of the few experiments in the book that is almost more like a magician's "reveal" than a process or a sequence of reactions—get it right and it just works. There is one more trick you can try, however…

# BALANCING ACT

## ADDITIONAL SETUP

The fact that you can balance a heavy fork and spoon on a tiny toothpick is pretty neat, but the best part is yet to come. Now, you want to balance the toothpick carefully on the edge of the glass. This will take a few tries, but eventually you'll find the correct balancing point and the two utensils will hang there, perfectly balanced.

You've probably been wondering what the matches are for, right? Well, if you want to take this experiment even further, make sure your spoon and fork are balanced on the edge of the glass and then strike the match. Light the end of the toothpick that's inside the glass and watch what happens. Once you've done that, light the other end of the toothpick.

To find the proper balancing point, we found that it was easier to adjust the toothpick, fork, and spoon so that the first was almost completely horizontal but the other two were leaning slightly downward.

## IN CONCLUSION

At the core of this experiment is the center of gravity. Many objects in the universe have one of these—the Earth, for example, rotates around its own center of gravity. In this example, it is the point on the length of the toothpick where all the weight of the associated objects—the toothpick, the fork, and the spoon—are perfectly in balance with each other. (The place where the toothpick touches the glass is also called the pivot point, defined as the point at which something balances or turns.)

If you've ever seen tightrope walkers, you'll have noticed that many of them use a long pole to help them keep their balance. The pole makes it easier for them to locate and maintain their own center of gravity more effectively.

The center of gravity was first hypothesized by the great Greek mathematician and engineer Archimedes (of bath tub, water displacement, "Eureka!" fame) who was born in 287 BCE. In fact, Archimedes called it the center of mass, and for many objects in many situations, this turns out to be exactly the same as the center of gravity, so long as gravity is acting uniformly on the object. Differences between the two occur, however, if the gravitational force is weaker toward the top of an object and stronger toward the bottom. In this case, the center of mass will be above the center of gravity.

When you burn the ends of the toothpick you may be surprised that the whole thing doesn't burn and the fork and spoon don't fall to the table. If you think about it, though, it's understandable why this doesn't happen. In order for fire to exist it needs three things: fuel (the toothpick), heat (which the fire generates), and oxygen. When the fire reaches either the glass or the metal of the utensils, they absorb the heat; without heat, the fire can't exist, so it just goes out.

# 19

# FLYING SAUCERS

## UFOs are real (and made of plastic)

**YOU WILL NEED:**
• Two Styrofoam™ plates, one slightly smaller than the other • Cotton cloth

If you use the same plates several times for this experiment, you'll notice that the electrical charge diminishes because the natural oils on your hands inhibit static electricity. Just start over with fresh plates.

## SETUP

Take the cotton cloth and use it to rub the bottom of each plate vigorously for about 30 seconds. Once you've done that, lay the larger plate face-down on the kitchen table. Take the smaller plate in one hand with the bottom facing down (so that you're trying to bring the bottoms of both plates together) and then place the palm of your other hand over the smaller plate. Let go of the smaller plate with your first hand and then, with your other hand, push it down toward the larger plate.

## TESTING

The "flying saucer" won't actually fly, but you'll discover that the two plates *really* don't want to have anything to do with each other. As you push down, you'll feel resistance as some unseen force pushes back. If you let go of the smaller plate it will shoot sideways away from the larger plate.

You can experiment by trying plates or bowls of different sizes. You could also see what difference it makes to rub them with the cotton cloth for longer. Does the effect persist or does the invisible force feel any stronger?

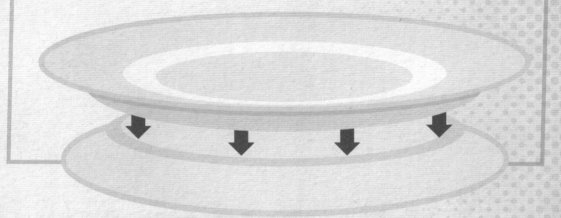

## IN CONCLUSION

The invisible force is static electricity. Styrofoam™ doesn't conduct electricity very well, so when you create the charge by rubbing it with the cotton cloth, it "sticks" to the plate. Styrofoam™ also has a tendency to become negatively charged, and since both plates are made of the same material, when you bring them together the like charges repel each other.

Static electricity has a part to play in the spray-painting of cars. Each droplet of paint receives a small electrical charge, while the part being painted receives a dose of the opposite charge. This allows the paint to be distributed across the surface of the part in a smooth, even fashion and also results in less wastage.

# 20

# KITCHEN SCAFFOLDING

## It's all a question of balance

**YOU WILL NEED:**
- Four empty drinking glasses (all the same size)
- Three table or butter knives (all the same size)
- Water

## SETUP

Place three empty glasses to form the three corners of a triangle. Space them so that they're slightly further away from each other than the length of your knives (so the knives can't be used to form a direct bridge between the glasses). Fill the fourth glass with water and somehow find a way to use the three empty glasses and knives to support the glass of water. Struggling?

## TESTING

This setup is a bit complicated to explain, so use the diagram opposite for reference. You have to arrange the knives like this: The tip of knife 1 sits over the middle of knife 2, forming a "T" shape. Then angle the second knife away from the center by about 30 degrees. Now take knife 3 and lay the tip over the middle of knife 1 and pull the tip of knife 2 over the top of the middle of knife 3. You should have an arrangement where the tip of each knife sits on top of the center of the next knife, and you can place this arrangement so that the handle of each knife rests on top of each glass. Now try placing a glass of water in the center.

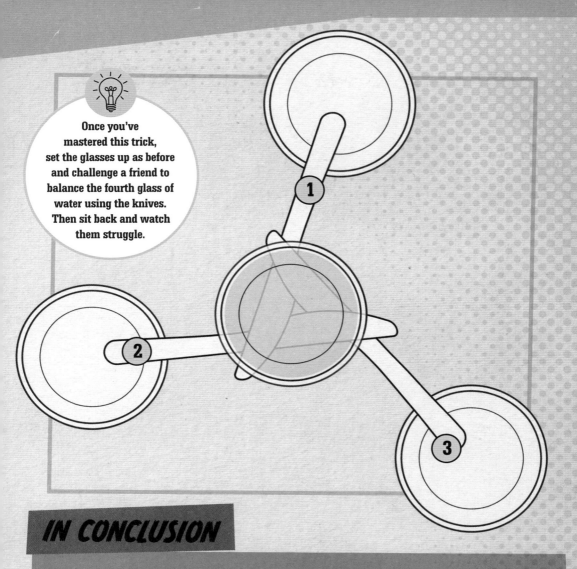

Once you've mastered this trick, set the glasses up as before and challenge a friend to balance the fourth glass of water using the knives. Then sit back and watch them struggle.

## IN CONCLUSION

Aside from being a clever trick that's been fooling people for years, this experiment is a great example of "balanced force," where the forces operating on a single object, or set of objects, are equal. In this instance, the force on the intertwined knives is being applied equally upward and downward, so they lock in place and won't move. In this arrangement, they're more than strong enough to support the glass of water.

The same thing happens in a tug of war, where two teams are pulling in opposite directions with equal force and the rope doesn't move: the forces are balanced. When one side gets the upper hand, the force becomes unbalanced and the rope will move in the direction of the team that is applying the greater force.

# #21 ⚠️ MAGIC ROUNDABOUT

## This thing's going nowhere, fast

**YOU WILL NEED:**
- AA battery
- Neodymium magnet the same diameter as the battery or slightly larger
- Uncoated copper wire
- Scissors

## SETUP

Cut about 6in (15cm) of copper wire and wrap it around your finger to make a spiral that will fit loosely over your battery. If you're using a magnet with a larger diameter than the battery, adjust the bottom of the spiral so it's slightly wider. Take the top of the wire and bend it over so it's pointing down. Sit the battery on top of the magnet, with the positive end facing up, and place both on the kitchen table. Carefully lower the wire spiral over the battery and balance the top of the wire on the top of the battery. Bend the bottom end of the wire in slightly, until it is just touching the magnet. Then let go.

## TESTING

When you let go of the wire, it should begin to spin around the battery—although you may need to give it a nudge to get it going.

If your roundabout is not going around and about, you could try flipping the magnet so it's the other way up. You may also need to bend the wire in a bit more at the bottom, to ensure that it's making full contact with the edge of the magnet.

You need to use a neodymium magnet for this because it packs more of a magnetic punch than an ordinary magnet. Neodymium magnets are cheap and easy to find online—bear in mind that it will be easier to set up the experiment with a magnet that is at least ¼ in thick.

## IN CONCLUSION

Congratulations! You've made a homopolar motor, which uses a combination of electricity and a magnetic field to work its magic. The result is thanks to something called the Lorentz force, named after Nobel Prize-winning Dutch physicist Hendrik A. Lorentz.

The electrical current flows from the top of the battery (the positive end) to the bottom (the negative end) and into the magnet. It then flows out to the edge of the magnet and up through the copper wire, and back into the top of the battery, thus completing the circuit. The electromagnetic force that Lorentz observed is the force on a moving charge (the flow of electrons through the circuit) in a magnetic field (created by the magnet). This force acts at right angles to the magnetic field, causing the wire to spin around the battery.

Homopolar motors are sometimes used in wind turbines because they don't need to use complex gearing systems and so are easy to maintain.

# LEMONADE FOUNTAIN

## Perfect for a summer picnic!

**YOU WILL NEED:**
- Empty 68fl oz (2l) plastic bottle with cap
- Empty 170fl oz (5l) plastic bottle with cap • Water
- Homemade lemonade
- Pushpin • Screwdriver (or something else to make a hole with)

## SETUP

Let's start by demonstrating the principle behind this experiment. Take the smaller 68fl oz (2l) bottle and fill it with water. Screw the top on nice and tight. Take the pushpin and, holding the bottle over the sink, make a single hole, about three inches from the bottom of the bottle. Watch what happens when you first make the hole and then what happens afterwards.

Next, make four additional holes in the bottle so they line up with the first one. Again, take a moment to observe what happens each time you make a hole.

Until you've perfected this, it's best to do all your setup in a sink. You know, just in case...

## TESTING

When you first poke a hole in the bottle, a little jet of water will shoot out, but this will soon subside. Even when you've poked five holes in the bottle, the same thing will happen: water comes out at first, then stops. Try squeezing the bottle a bit and you'll see that water pours out of the holes freely. Stop squeezing and the flow stops.

Next, instead of squeezing the bottle, just unscrew the cap and see what happens to the flow of water, and then check the result when you screw the cap back on. It's like opening and closing a tap: the water flows and then it stops.

Finally, unscrew the cap and once the water is flowing out of the holes, run a finger horizontally across them. You'll notice that only the last hole in the line stays "open" and that water stops flowing from the other holes. Run your finger in the opposite direction and the same thing happens in reverse. Now, run your finger over all the holes from top to bottom. Suddenly, water is flowing from all the holes again. What's going on?

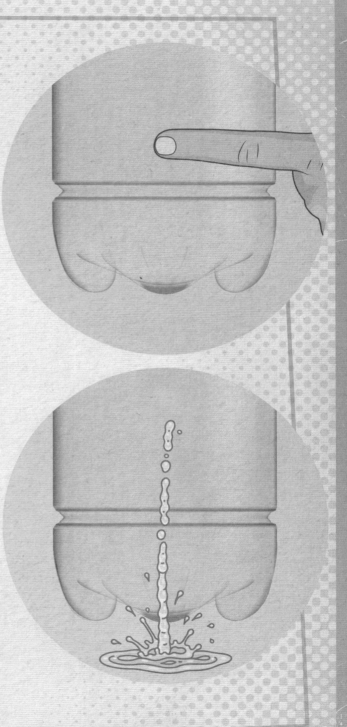

# LEMONADE FOUNTAIN

**Make sure you use a clean bottle!**

If you're having a "can't be bothered" moment, just substitute lemon drink mix for homemade lemonade. Add a couple of slices of fresh lemon before closing the cap and your guests may be none the wiser.

## ADDITIONAL SETUP

Now you've perfected the technique, why not make a portable lemonade fountain that you can take into the backyard on hot summer days? Start by following a recipe to make your lemonade and then take an empty 170fl oz (5l) plastic bottle and carefully use the screwdriver to make a tap-sized hole in it, about 2in (5cm) from the bottom. Next, cover the hole with your thumb and get someone else to fill the bottle with lemonade. When they're done, screw the top on firmly and, keeping your thumb over the hole, get them to help you carry it out to the backyard. Hold a glass under the hole and remove your thumb. Collect the lemonade as it shoots out. After a moment or two, it'll stop flowing and you're ready to go. Any time someone wants a glass of lemonade, just unscrew the cap a little and your "fountain" will do the rest!

## IN CONCLUSION

When you poke a hole in the bottle, enough air molecules are able to sneak in so that the water (or lemonade) flows out briefly. Pretty soon though—thanks to the screwed-on cap—there's simply not enough space for the air to enter and the water stops flowing. When you unscrew the top, more air can get in. It pushes down on the surface of the water/lemonade and, together with gravity, provides enough force to make the liquid flow again. When you screw the top back on the pressure slowly equalizes and the flow stops.

So, what's going on when you pass your finger across or up and down over those five small holes? It's all to do with surface tension: the tendency of a fluid like water to assume the smallest surface area possible. As you pass your finger from left to right you're blocking each of the holes in turn, just long enough so that the water continues seeking the easiest way out of the bottle. So, as hole one is closed, the water goes to holes two, three, four, and five. As each hole is closed by your finger, a drop of water "sticks" in the hole and acquires enough surface tension to create a temporary seal. Move your finger back the other way and the reverse happens. Move your finger down or up over the row of holes and you "burst" all those little water seals and the water flows through each hole again.

# #23 ⚠

# TEA LIGHT BOILER

## Heat a small room with a single candle!

**YOU WILL NEED:**
- Old plate • Old saucer
- Unglazed terra-cotta pot matched in size to the plate and saucer
- Small candle (such as a tea light) • Matches
- 15 pennies

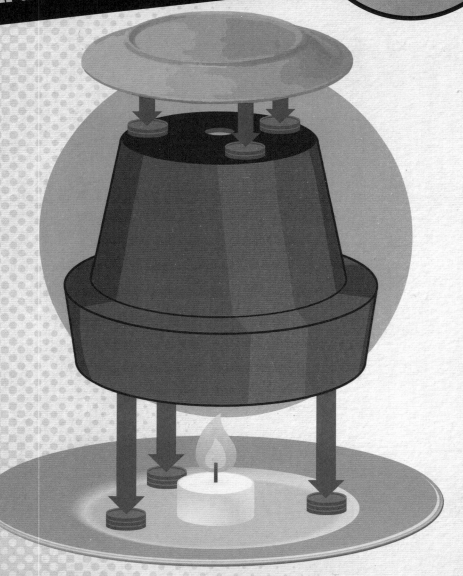

## SETUP

Do this either on the kitchen floor or on a table, if you don't mind possibly marking it. Pop the plate down and then place three piles of three cents each to make the corners of a triangle. Look at the size of the open end of the terra-cotta pot to judge how far apart to place them—you want your pot to be able to sit on the coins. Next, place the tea light (or other small candle) in the center of the plate and light it with a match. Place the upturned pot over the candle so it balances on the piles of pennies.

Now, take the six remaining coins and, being careful not to touch the pot with your hands (it will already be very hot), make three piles of two pennies, again, marking out the corners of a triangle on top of the pot. Finally, take the saucer, turn it upside down, and place it over the top of the pot so it rests on the coins.

## TESTING

Your boiler will get remarkably hot, very quickly. You'll notice that the heat seems to come from all around the pot, although it will be hotter at the top. The other thing to note is that the pot and plates will stay hot for some time, even after the candle has gone out.

**Your boiler will get hot—seriously hot—so make sure you test it in an area that's safe, where little fingers can't accidentally touch it and curious pets won't be tempted to inspect it.**

# TEA LIGHT BOILER

## YOU WILL NEED— INDUSTRIAL VERSION:
- Large unglazed terra-cotta pot • Smaller unglazed terra-cotta pot • 6in (15cm) hex bolt about ½in (1.3cm) across
- Two hex nuts • Four washers
- Three bricks • Two short candles • Old plate

## ADDITIONAL TESTING

If you want to build a boiler with
a bit more oomph, you're going need
bigger pots—well, bigger everything,
really. We've listed everything you'll
need opposite. Here's how to put it
all together.

First, arrange the bricks to form three
sides of a square and place the old
plate in the middle. Pop the candles
on the plate. Next you want to slide
a washer onto the hex bolt and thread
it through the bottom of the largest
pot. Turn the pot the right way up
and drop a washer down the bolt
on the inside of the pot and then
screw on the first of the hex nuts.
Drop another washer down the bolt
and then take the smaller pot and
put it inside the larger pot so the bolt
comes through the hole. Add the last
washer and nut and you're nearly done.
(To double check, the order should
go like this: bolt, washer, largest pot,
washer, hex nut, washer, small pot,
washer, hex nut.)

Light the candles, upturn the double
pot contraption so it sits on the three
bricks and enjoy the toastiness!
(Optimum toastiness will take about
30–40 minutes to achieve.)

## IN CONCLUSION

These heaters work thanks to
two different factors. The first is
convection. This is the tendency of
anything that is hot—in this case
air—to move in a circular motion so
the less dense molecules rise and the
cooler ones drop down. In our small,
basic heater, the air heated inside
the pot rises up through the hole, but
instead of rising to the ceiling and
dissipating, it circulates underneath
the plate, moving outward and
spreading the warmth.

In the industrial version, the hex
bolt prevents the air from rising up
through the pots, but it still needs
to rise, so it pushes itself out, under
the rim of the inner pot, from where
it rises again, trying to get out of the
top of the outer pot. Since it can't do
that either, it pushes out around the
bottom rim of the outer pot and then
radiates out into the room.

This brings us to the second factor
at work. Terra-cotta is really good at
retaining heat and releasing it slowly.
This is particularly important for the
second heater because of the double
pot construction, which heats up the
inner and outer sleeves of both pots,
making it very efficient.

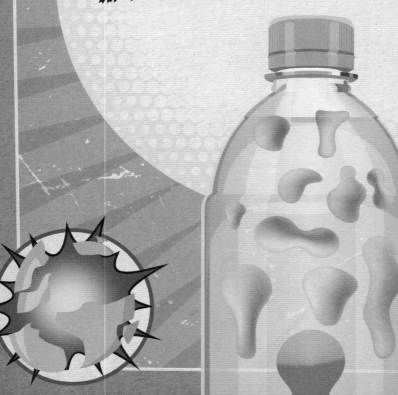

PART 3

# MARVELOUS MIXTURES

# CONTENTS

# #24 ⚠
# THE POT THAT NEVER BOILS OVER

## It'll go dry first

## SETUP

Set the saucepan on the stove, fill it three-quarters full of water and turn up the heat. Wait until the water has begun to boil and then—carefully—lay the wooden utensil across the top of the saucepan. As the water starts to achieve a rolling boil and bubbles begin to form, you stand back, expecting that the pot will soon boil over and flood the top of the stove. You wait with paper towels at the ready to mop up the mess, but what actually happens?

## TESTING

In fact, when the bubbles reach fever pitch, instead of boiling over, they retreat half-heartedly back into the saucepan, seemingly biding their time until they feel like having another go. At this point the same thing happens all over again, and it will continue until the pan boils dry.

You can try adding food to the pan to see if that makes any difference to the outcome, but we're pretty sure it won't, unless there's a lot of starch in what you're cooking—pasta or rice or potatoes, for example. In this case the starch may "strengthen" the bubbles and some may be able to escape over the top of the pan. Most will not, however.

## IN CONCLUSION

There are two things happening here. First, if you use a wooden utensil that has a coating on it, this will make the surface hydrophobic, which means that it won't absorb water, so the bubbles burst and what's inside doesn't get absorbed into the utensil. Second, these bubbles aren't filled with air; they're filled with steam, and that means they're hot—really hot—and very thermodynamically unstable. When the surface of the bubbles comes into contact with anything colder than they are (that is, less than 212°F, or 100°C) then the steam condenses and they pop. For fun, remove the utensil and try blowing on the bubbles as they rise toward the edge of the pan. Again, they'll burst, because your breath is colder than 212°F (100°C).

This technique is used all the time in busy restaurant kitchens, where it saves easily distracted chefs from having pans that constantly boil over.

## PUZZLER!?!

You can also experiment with using a metal utensil instead of a wooden one. Bearing in mind the information given in the conclusion, what do you think will happen?

# WE JUST DON'T GET ALONG

## Sometimes hot and cold just don't mix

## SETUP

Fill one of the glasses to the top with cold water and fill the other to the top with warm water. Add a drop of blue food dye to the cold water and a drop of yellow to the warm water. Give them both a stir. Place the card on top of the glass of warm (yellow) water, then holding the card in place, upturn the glass and place both over the glass of cold (blue) water. Remove the card by sliding it out from between the two glasses. What happens to the water?

Empty the glasses out and start again, but this time, upturn the playing card and glass with the cold water (and blue dye) on top of the glass of warm water (and yellow food dye). Remove the card again and watch what happens now.

## TESTING

The first time around, the two colors will barely mix at all. There'll be some "will they won't they" uncertainty where the two meet, but that will soon settle down and you'll clearly be able to see the yellow water layered on top of the blue. However, when things are reversed, and the warm water is on the bottom, the contents of the two glasses mix almost as soon as you remove the card, so you end up with water that's green from top to bottom.

## IN CONCLUSION

The molecules in warm water move around more quickly than those in cold water. That means they bounce around all over the place, hitting each other and moving further apart, which results in more space between the molecules. More space means that the volume of warm water weighs less than the equivalent cold water and it therefore rises. With the cold water on the bottom and warm on top, the two are already occupying their natural places, but when you put the glass of warm water on the bottom and the cold on top, the warm water rises, mixing with the cold. Hence the yellow and blue liquids turn a lovely shade of green.

# SUGAR RAINBOW

## Creating you own rainbow is pretty sweet

**YOU WILL NEED:**
- Sugar • Measuring spoon
- Long-handled spoon for stirring • Six drinking glasses
- Food dye (preferably in six different colors) • Warm water
- Clear straw

OPTIONAL:
- Turkey baster
- Extra glass

## SETUP

Line up your empty glasses on a table or the kitchen counter and then fill each of them with warm water to about ½in (1.3cm) from the top. Add food dye to each glass of water. If you can find six different colors, that's great, but if not you can use slightly different amounts of one color—say, red—to produce different shades, for example, from a light pink through to a deep crimson. Leaving the first glass as it is, add one spoonful of sugar to the second glass, two spoonfuls to the third glass, three to the fourth, four to the fifth, and five to the sixth. Stir each one as you go to make sure the sugar completely dissolves.

# TESTING

Take the straw and pop the end into the first glass—the one with no sugar in it—and then cover the top of the straw with your thumb. Take it out of the glass and, keeping the top covered with your thumb, pop it 1in (2.5cm) or so into the second glass (the one with a single spoonful of sugar in it). Very quickly, take your thumb off the top of the straw and put it back on again immediately. Pull the straw out of the glass and take a look. If you did it right, you'll see you've sucked up a second layer of water. Now do the same with the remaining four glasses. When you get to the end, check out the straw. There's your rainbow.

**Don't skimp on the stirring. For this experiment to work properly, the sugar needs to be completely dissolved in the water.**

# SUGAR RAINBOW

## ADDITIONAL SETUP

This takes a bit more care and is subject to some trial and error. (Some testers say you'll need the hands of a surgeon!) Take your turkey baster and, this time, start with the glass that contains the most sugar—the sixth glass. This is important: using the straw, you start with the glass that has no sugar; using the baster, you reverse the process and start with the glass that has the *most* sugar.

Suck some water from the glass into the turkey baster and then squirt it out into the empty glass. Rinse out the baster with warm water. Then suck up some from the fifth glass and, very carefully, place the nozzle of the baster against the side of the glass, just above the surface of the liquid that's already there. Now very gently squeeze out the water from the turkey baster. Rinse the baster again. Continue until you've added water from the remaining four glasses. If your hands were steady enough, you should now have a glass filled with a liquid rainbow.

# IN CONCLUSION

It's finally here, your date with density. Yes, that's what this experiment is all about, the different densities of the various sugar solutions. Density equals mass (that is, the substance of the object you're dealing with) divided by volume (that is, the space that the substance occupies). The more sugar you add to the water, the denser it becomes, and denser liquids will sink in the same way that less dense liquids will rise. This explains why the liquids remain separated in the glass when you use the turkey baster: because you begin with the water that has the most sugar in it—the most dense—and work your way up.

When you use the straw to suck up the liquids, slightly different factors are at play. First, similar molecules (for example, water molecules) like to stick together; this is called cohesion. Second, water molecules like to cling to other kinds of molecules (like those making up the end of the straw); this is known as adhesion. When you place your thumb over the end of the straw, you eliminate the air pressue from the top. This makes the air pressure inside the straw lower than the air pressure outside it. As soon as you take your thumb away, the air pressure inside and out will equalize, and then gravity takes over and the water pours out.

Water molecule

Sugar molecule

It can be tempting to rush when adding the color layers, but be patient and take your time. Squeeze the turkey baster slowly and slide it gently up the wall of the glass as the liquid level rises.

# MILKALEIDOSCOPE

## A light show on your plate

**YOU WILL NEED:**
- Small plate • Enough full-fat milk to cover the plate
- Three or four different colors of food dye
- Two Q-tips
- Dish soap

## SETUP

Pour milk onto the plate—just enough to cover the surface will do. Next, add a single drop of each color of food dye as if you were marking out the three points of a triangle (if you're using three colors) or the four corners of a square (if you're using four). Keep them close together toward the middle of the plate. Next, take the Q-tip and dip it into the middle of the milk/food dye mixture. What happens when you do?

Now, take the second clean Q-tip and dip it in some dish soap—you want to be able to see a good-size drop hanging off the end. Dip the end of the Q-tip with the dish soap into the milk at the center of the plate. Does adding dish soap make any difference?

## TESTING

You bet it does! At first the Q-tip doesn't really do anything; the fluffy cotton end may absorb some of the liquid, but otherwise it's all a bit uneventful. By adding the dish soap you create a moving kaleidoscope of color, where the mixture of milk and food dye shoots away from the Q-tip and continues moving, mixing, and creating new colors.

## IN CONCLUSION

Although it's mainly made up of water, milk does contain droplets of fat. When you add the drop of dish soap to the mixture, it starts a chemical reaction that causes the fat and soap molecules to be attracted to each other. In fact, they're attracted to each other so strongly that they push everything else out of the way— hence the kaleidoscopic color show. At first, this happens very quickly, but as the two combine, the reaction slows down and eventually stops.

## PUZZLER!?!

Do you expect the same result if you try the same experiment with skimmed milk?

# #28

# CLASSIC LAVA LAMP

## Going back to the '70s, baby!

## SETUP

Take the label off the plastic bottle and clean it a little. Then dry it off and pour in the water until it's about one-quarter full. Top it up with the vegetable oil so it's nearly—but not quite—full to the top. You'll notice that despite some initial sloshing back and forth as you add the oil, it doesn't actually mix with the water; indeed, if you let things settle for five minutes you'll see that the two become clearly separated, with the water on the bottom and the oil on top.

Next, add about six drops of liquid food dye into the mixture. Notice that it sinks through the oil until it reaches the water, which absorbs it—only the water absorbs the color and not the oil. Finally, break the Alka-Seltzer tablet into four pieces and drop one of them in. Let it sink to the bottom of the bottle. What do you think is going to happen?

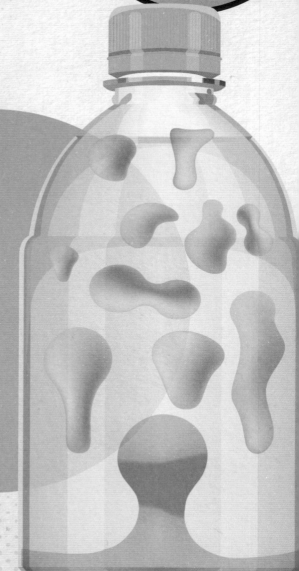

## TESTING

When you add the oil, it will eventually settle and sit on top of the water. In fact, it's proving the old adage "oil and water don't mix." When you add the food coloring it only colors the water and not the oil. When you drop the bit of Alka-Seltzer tablet into the bottle, bubbles start rising up to the surface from the bottom—carrying the food coloring with them—and then tumbling back down to the bottom, where the whole thing starts over again.

When the bubbles subside, just drop in another bit of tablet and things will kick off again. When you've used all four pieces of tablet, screw the top onto the bottle firmly and then give it a good shake. What happens now?

You can also place the bottle on a glass table and hold the flashlight underneath, so it shines up through the bottle.

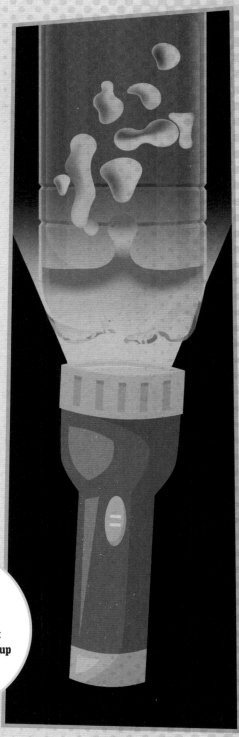

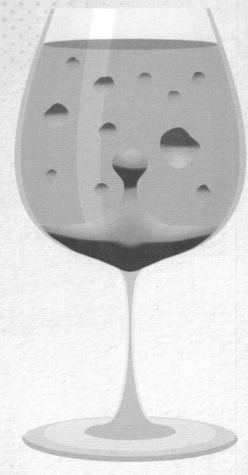

## ADDITIONAL SETUP

Instead of using a single bottle, you could also use several large wine glasses. Fill each one-quarter full with water, then add vegetable oil, but this time, add a different color of food coloring to each glass. Once things have settled, add the Alka-Seltzer pieces to each glass in turn.

You can also try this in a darkened room. Set the glasses bubbling and then turn the lights out. Shine the flashlight behind each of the glasses in turn and check out the effect. It will look even more like a lava lamp than before.

So, the old saying is true: oil and water really don't mix—they don't mix at all. In fact, they won't even mix when you shake the bottle vigorously. Rather, the oil stays in globules and wobbles about in the water until the liquids eventually separate into two layers. The oil floats because it's less dense than water and so rises to the top of the bottle or glass.

Water molecules are strongly attracted to other water molecules because they're what's known as polar molecules. Oil, on the other hand, is made up of non-polar molecules, which are hydrophobic—literally, "afraid of water"—so the two substances don't mix.

Food coloring dissolves in water, but not in oil. When you drop the Alka-Seltzer tablet into the bottle, it reacts with the water to create minuscule bubbles of carbon dioxide, which rise up through the oil, carrying some colored water with them, until they reach the surface and burst. Then the water droplets fall back through the oil to the bottom, and the whole reaction begins again.

**Depending on how agitated the mixture becomes when you add the oil to the water, you may want to leave things to settle down for longer than five minutes. This is more fun if the two liquids are completely separated.**

# 29

# PEEL POPPER

## It's official: oranges hate balloons

**YOU WILL NEED:**
- A thick-skinned orange
- Several balloons of different sizes

## SETUP

Start by blowing up your balloons and knotting their ends. Inflate them to different sizes so you can see if this makes any difference to the results. Next, take your orange and tear off a good-sized chunk of the peel. Hold it over the first balloon with the skin pointing at the balloon. Give it a good squeeze so the juice inside the skin comes out in a fine spray. See what we mean about the age-old feud between oranges and balloons?

## TESTING

There are several tests you could do for this experiment. You can pop individual balloons, as we've suggested, or you can tie a bunch of balloons together and see how easy it is to burst them all. You could bet a gullible friend that you can burst a balloon with an orange—without throwing it—and see how much money you can make! You could try using other citrus fruits, like lemons or limes. You could even see if it'll work with orange juice from a carton. What do you think will happen if you do?

## IN CONCLUSION

Oranges contain a chemical called limonene—the substance that gives oranges their wonderful citrus smell—which is made up almost entirely of carbon and hydrogen; in other words, it's a hydrocarbon. Rubber is also a hydrocarbon, which means it has another characteristic in common with limonene: they are both non-polar substances. Scientists have a saying, "like dissolves like," which means that a non-polar substances dissolves well in another non-polar substance. In this case, the limonene is highly concentrated and is strong enough to dissolve the rubber in the balloon when it makes contact. This weakens the surface of the balloon and it bursts. Flicking orange juice from a carton at a balloon won't do anything, by the way—apart from making it sticky.

Rubber balloons were first developed in 1824 at the London laboratory of the scientist Michael Faraday, who was researching the properties of hydrogen. These balloons were a definite improvement on earlier versions, which had been made from animal bladders, sewn with vegetable thread to produce an airtight seal, and tied off with intestines.

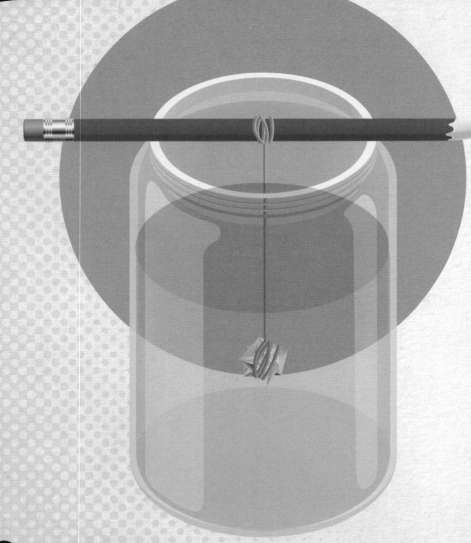

# #30
# CRYSTAL MAGIC

## Beautiful crystals grown in a jar

**YOU WILL NEED:**
- Alum • Teaspoon • Two jars
- Hot water • Plastic twine
(fishing line will do) • Pencil
(or craft stick) • Paper towel or
thin cloth • Rubber band

OPTIONAL:
- Food dye

# SETUP

Fill the first jar with hot water and stir in three or four teaspoons of alum, making sure it dissolves fully. Keep adding more teaspoonfuls until the water can't take any more and the alum stops dissolving. Now cover the jar with a paper towel or cloth, secure it with the rubber band, and leave it until the next day.

When you come back, look carefully at the bottom of the jar and you'll see that tiny crystals—called "starters"—have formed already. It's pretty neat, but we want more. Very carefully, pour the alum solution into the empty jar, being very careful not to mess up those baby crystals nestling at the bottom of the jar.

Pick the largest one and secure it with a loop of plastic twine, then attach that to the pencil or craft stick, making sure the distance between the crystal and the pencil is less than the height of the jar. Drop the crystal into the jar containing the alum mixture and lay the pencil across the top. The crystal should be suspended in the liquid, not touching the bottom or sides of the jar. Cover this again with the paper towel and rubber band to keep out any foreign bodies.

**Securing the baby crystal to the twine is a pain in the you-know-what. But don't be tempted to use cotton—which is easier—because the crystals will simply grow along the thread in a chain.**

# TESTING

We've already started growing crystals, by leaving the first jar overnight to create our baby "starter," but now the real fun starts. Check back on your crystal each day to see how much it has grown. You may want to remove it from the solution periodically and move it around so it grows outward in all directions and forms a uniform shape; if you're not bothered what shape it makes, you can just leave it. One thing you must do, however, is to remove any new crystals that form in the bottom of the jar, as these will "steal" growth away from the main one, meaning that it won't grow to its full potential size. Just pour the solution out into a fresh jar, leaving the baby crystals behind, and start another cycle.

# CRYSTAL MAGIC

Alum has various uses, from pickling, where it keeps cucumbers crisp, to helping you stay fresh (you can buy alum deodorant). Although it's available from the spice section of larger Asian grocers (where it's sometimes called fatakdi powder), don't eat it—it tastes horrid.

Normally, when you add enough of a substance to water that it will no longer dissolve, you make a saturated solution. However, by using hot water, we're able to dissolve more of the alum than we would be able to in cold water. This is because the heated water molecules move apart, leaving room for more of the alum to dissolve. The result is called a super-saturated solution. You're left with lots of alum sitting in hot water, waiting for something to happen.

That "something" is cooling. As the water cools, it becomes unable to hold all of the alum molecules in the solution, so they begin to form crystals; these are the baby crystals—the starters—you see at the bottom of the first jar.

When you transfer the single biggest crystal to the new jar of solution, the process continues. As the alum molecules move out of the solution they stick to the larger crystal, attaching themselves to its edges. It's important to make sure your crystal is suspended and doesn't touch anything apart from the plastic twine, otherwise the alum molecules will attach to the other objects too.

## ADDITIONAL SETUP

Once you've grown your crystal you can mount it on a necklace—if you have the craft skills—or take it to a jewelry-making shop and have them do it. You'll end up with a unique gift for someone—or for yourself!

You can also create colored crystals by adding a few drops of food dye to the solution. To produce really brightly colored crystals, do this at the beginning of the crystallization process to give the color as much time as possible to be absorbed into the solution. Or, if you'd like just a hint of color, add a single drop of food dye, to give your crystal a pastel hue.

# WALKING WATER

## Move water between glasses without touching it

**YOU WILL NEED:**
- Three drinking glasses of the same size • Paper towel
- Water • Blue and yellow food dyes

OPTIONAL:
- Iceberg lettuce • Scissors
- Red food dye • Two more glasses of the same size

## SETUP

Take a couple of sheets of paper towel and fold them lengthways so that they're narrow enough to fit comfortably into the open mouth of your drinking glasses; this will probably be 1–2in (2.5–5cm) wide. Take your three glasses and place them on the kitchen table in a row, 2–3in (5–7.6cm) apart. Half fill the two glasses at either end and leave the middle one empty. Add a couple of drops of blue food dye to one of the end glasses and a couple of drops of yellow food dye to the glass at the other end. You should now have a row of three glasses: half-full with blue water, empty, and half-full with yellow water.

Take one strip of paper towel and put one end in the blue glass so it goes into the water and put the other end into the empty glass. Take the second length of towel and place one end in the yellow glass and the other end in the empty glass. That's it— you're all done.

Want to produce some different colors? Try mixing red and blue to get a nice royal purple or red and yellow to get orange, or turn to the "additional setup" on the following page to find out how to create multiple colors at once.

# TESTING

Things will start to happen almost immediately. The first thing you'll notice is that water from both the blue glass and the yellow glass slowly begins to "climb" up the paper towels and out of the glasses. You'll have seen something similar if you've ever lowered a piece of paper towel into a pool of liquid that's been spilled—it immediately rises up the towel.

Tempting as it might be to watch things happen, leave the glasses alone for a couple of hours. When you come back to it, you'll find that things have changed somewhat. In fact, you'll see that the water from both the blue and yellow glasses has climbed up the paper towels, across the divide between the glasses and down into the middle glass. That glass— previously empty—is now about one-quarter full of green water, which is the natural result of mixing blue and yellow together. So what went on while your back was turned?

## ADDITIONAL SETUP

If you fancy creating more of a rainbow effect, increase the number of glasses to five and add two more kitchen towels. Add food dye so the water/glass combo goes like this: yellow, empty, blue, empty, red. Fold up the kitchen towels as before and place them to act as bridges between the glasses following the instructions in the original setup, then leave this alone for a couple of hours. You'll end up with a row of glasses that goes yellow, green, blue, purple, and red.

It's not just paper towels that can move water, however. To see another example for yourself, remove the paper towels from the glasses, so you're left with your five glasses of colored water. Tear off five large pieces of iceberg lettuce and then cut across them at the bottom at a slight angle. Put one in each of the glasses and leave them for a couple of days. You'll see each one take on the color of the water in its glass.

# IN CONCLUSION

This experiment is a great example of capillary action at work. Normally, substances like water flow because of an external force—usually gravity. That's why rivers flow downhill. There are certain situations, however, where liquid can move without gravity or any other external force being involved, and this is one of them.

We've talked about adhesion and cohesion elsewhere (see page 89) and it comes into play here too. The walls of the paper towel attract the water molecules more strongly than the water molecules can attract each other, so the water wants to adhere to the towel more than it wants to stick together with the other water molecules. This creates the "climbing" effect, whereby the water moves inexorably up the towels and out of the glass. The levels of water in the glasses want to equalize, so water carries on flowing until the level is the same in all of the glasses.

There are examples of capillary action all over the place. One of the most obvious is the way that plants draw water up from the ground through their stems (as the lettuce leaves do in our experiment), but you'll also find it in the human body, such as in tear ducts, for example.

## PUZZLER!?!

Why cut the lettuce at a slight angle across the bottom?

# LIQUID OR SOLID?

## This stuff can't make up its mind!

**YOU WILL NEED:**
- Bowl for mixing
- Cornstarch • Water
- Food dye • Cup

Gunk too much like powder? Add more water. Too sloppy? Add more cornstarch.

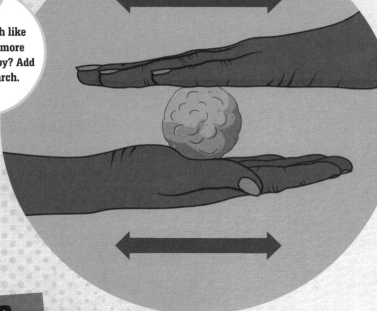

## SETUP

Pour a cupful of cornstarch into the bowl and then add a couple of drops of the food coloring. Slowly add half a cup of water, mixing the cornstarch and the food coloring into the water as you go. From time to time, tap the surface of the mixture sharply with your finger. To begin with, it'll feel a bit like tapping pudding—all soft and gooey. Keep tapping, though, and something strange will happen. When it does, you'll know the mixture is ready.

## TESTING

Once the mixture—let's call it gunk—has reached the right consistency, you can start to have some fun. Scoop some of it out of the bowl and mold it into a ball between your hands. So long as you keep up the pressure, it'll stay in the shape of a ball. When it's nice and solid, simply hold it flat in the palm of your hand or drop it onto the kitchen countertop and watch what happens. That solid ball will turn into a splat of liquid. Even more bizarrely, you can still gather it up with your fingers and mold it back into a ball again. When you do, drop it back into the bowl with the rest of the gunk and let it settle. Try punching it firmly and see what happens.

## IN CONCLUSION

Liquids are supposed to flow at a constant, predictable rate, but what you've created here only looks like a liquid. In fact, it's not a liquid at all, but a suspension: gazillions of tiny cornstarch particles hanging suspended in the water. This results in some really rather odd properties. For example, if you put the gunk under pressure (such as by shaping it into a ball) you increase its viscosity. The cornstarch particles are forced together and squeeze the water out of the way, so the gunk feels solid. Left to its own devices (i.e. under no pressure) it will behave more like a conventional liquid, filling the bowl or turning into a puddle on the countertop.

It was Sir Isaac Newton who first theorized that liquids flow at constant rates—that's why your gunk is known as a non-Newtonian liquid.

# DIY FIRE EXTINGUISHER

## Who needs the fire brigade?

**YOU WILL NEED:**
- Jug • Teaspoon
- Baking soda • White vinegar • Four or five tea light candles • Lighter or matches

**OPTIONAL:**
- Five extra tea lights
- Larger candle

## SETUP

Place the jug on the kitchen table or a countertop. Add a couple of teaspoons of baking soda to the jug and then slowly pour about an inch of white vinegar into the jug. There's no need to stir or mix the ingredients. Stop pouring as soon as the mixture begins to froth, as you don't want it to bubble over. Set that to one side for a moment to let the effervescing madness calm down a bit. Next, line up the tea lights along the table or countertop and then light them with the lighter or matches. You're ready to put out the fire.

## TESTING

Now, you could simply blow the candles out one by one, but we've got a more interesting way. Take the jug and, holding it just above the flame, tip it towards the first candle. You want to make sure that no liquid actually pours out—that's not the point of the experiment. Instead, just pass the spout of the jug over the first, then the second, third, and fourth candles, until you've passed it over all of them, and watch what happens.

As the spout of the jug nears each candle flame they are extinguished in turn, as if by magic.

This is one of the few experiments where we recommend you don't stir the ingredients together. That's because there's a chance that if you do, you'll stir the carbon dioxide either to the sides of the jug or out of it completely, which will reduce the efficacy of your fire extinguisher.

## ADDITIONAL SETUP

If you want to introduce a bit of drama into this experiment, try this demonstration at night. Start by increasing the number of tea lights to around 10. Line them up and place a much larger candle at the end. Make up the white vinegar/baking soda mixture as described in the original setup and light all your candles. Turn all the lights off, so the kitchen is in darkness, and then extinguish the candles with the jug, starting with the tea lights and ending with the giant candle at the end. It will produce a pretty dramatic effect. Just what is it that's "pouring" from the jug, and why does it have such an immediate effect on the flames?

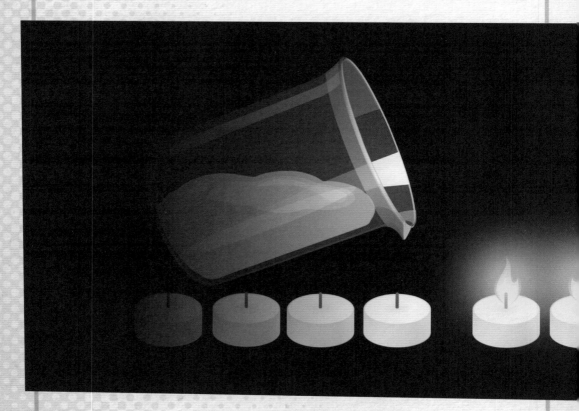

# IN CONCLUSION

Elsewhere we've talked about the fact that fire needs three elements to burn: namely, oxygen, fuel, and heat (see page 65). These three components are sometimes called the triangle of fire, or the combustion triangle. Take away one of them—any of them—and the fire goes out.

When you mix vinegar with baking soda, you're mixing a weak acid with a base, and they combine to produce carbonic acid. Carbonic acid is a bit bonkers. It's very unstable and quickly breaks down to form water and carbon dioxide—lots of carbon dioxide, in fact, so much that it pushes all the other gases out of the jug, filling it completely.

Given that carbon dioxide is heavier than air, when you tip the jug over the candle flame, the carbon dioxode "pours" out like water, and overwhelms any oxygen feeding the flame, putting it out immediately.

Commercial carbon dioxide fire extinguishers—the red ones with black hoses and "horns" that you see in public buildings everywhere—work on the same principle. They spray out compressed carbon dioxide at tremendous speed and are extremely effective at dealing with electrical fires or fires involving flammable liquids like petrol. They shouldn't be used, however, for things like deep-fat fryer fires, because they shoot the carbon dioxide gas out so fast that there's a danger of spraying burning oil all over the place.

Oh, and remember the carbonic acid that was produced when you first mixed vinegar and baking soda? It may sound dangerous, but in fact you've probably ingested it before—it's found in most carbonated soft drinks.

## PART 4

# TERRIFIC TRANSITIONS

# CONTENTS

# #34

## COAL INTO DIAMOND

### A jewel for the price of a jar of peanut butter?

**YOU WILL NEED:**
• Hot barbecue coal • Large jar of smooth peanut butter • Bowl • Ice cubes • Bowl of warm water • Metal tongs • Safety goggles • Gardening gloves

To start, you need a barbecue coal that's hot from the fire (rather than hot from the oven) so it may be best to do this experiment when you're having a barbecue. The coal should be just starting to turn white at the edges—this ensures it's at the correct temperature. Open the jar of peanut butter, put on the gardening gloves, and use the tongs to pick up the coal and dunk it into the peanut butter. Scooch it around until it's completely covered in peanut butter. Take the coal out of the jar and pop it in the bowl of ice. Add more ice cubes so the coal is completely covered and then leave it for 24 hours.

After 24 hours the ice will probably have melted (that's fine). Take the coal/peanut-butter ball out from the icy water that's left and drop it into the warm water. What do you think will happen?

Don't use crunchy peanut butter—the little shards of peanut contain oils that inhibit the crystal-growing process.

# COAL INTO DIAMOND

## TESTING

Leave the peanut-butter ball in the warm water for five minutes and then use your bare hands (it won't be hot any more) to rub away the coating of peanut butter. It may still be stuck to the coal, but you'll be able to ease it off with just your fingers. What you'll be left with is something that looks a little like the coal you started with, except that the surface is somehow loose and a bit slippery, as if it was a skin, covering something.

Keep rubbing with your fingers and this outer "skin" will peel away to reveal what's inside. It's a beautiful—quite stunning, in fact—crystal that you've created from your piece of barbecue coal. Wow!

# IN CONCLUSION

Scientists have known for years that coal and diamonds are both forms of carbon. Indeed, if you were able to travel down into the earth for about 100 miles (160km), you'd find lots of what was originally coal being turned into diamonds, thanks to the enormous heat (thousands of degrees) and incredible pressure. For a while now, labs have been experimenting with ways to duplicate this process and that's kind of what's happening here. It sounds like a bit of a stretch—but stay with us.

Peanut butter is rich in carbon. When you place it in the ice and cover it, the temperature plummets and causes a reaction. The oxygen is extracted from the carbon dioxide present in the peanut butter, leaving behind only carbon dioxide, which exerts massive pressure on the coal inside—equivalent to 130,000 atmospheres. Similar to what's going on beneath the surface of the earth, this pressure "purifies" the coal and encourages crystallization, which transforms the coal cells into crystal cells. This transformation is a very delicate process and can be affected by the impurities in crunchy peanut butter—hence you have to use smooth.

Why do you still have to rub off the outer skin? Adhesion makes the outer layer of carbon more resistant to the purifying process and so that coal retains this thin surface layer, which can be sloughed off with your fingers, much as a snake sheds its skin.

Unfortunately, despite its superficial good looks, your "diamond" isn't actually worth anything—if it was, we'd all be rich—but it's a superb and surprising memento for you to keep and commemorate your scientific adventures.

Well, we did warn you that one of the experiments in *Kitchen Sink Science* was bogus—and you've found it. While coal and diamonds are indeed both forms of carbon, and carbon *is* turned into diamonds under extreme pressure, it's not possible to recreate the conditions needed at home—a bowl of ice certainly isn't able to exert the same pressure as 130,000 atmospheres. The Internet is awash with stuff like this, phony science designed to distract you for a moment or two with something shiny that sounds *just* plausible enough to investigate. Suffice to say, if you've managed to extract a diamond from coal using peanut butter, we'd love to hear about it!

# 35

# BEAKER BEGONE

## Now you see it, now you don't

**YOU WILL NEED:**
• Large Pyrex beaker
• Small Pyrex beaker
• 32fl oz (1l) vegetable oil • A friend—if you want to freak them out!

## SETUP

Place the larger beaker on the kitchen table and then place the smaller beaker inside it. Start by filling the smaller beaker with vegetable oil. Be careful not to let any spill out into the larger beaker because this will spoil the effect—and the fun. With the setup complete, you can still see both beakers quite clearly, right? Now you're ready to get testing.

## TESTING

Make sure your friend is watching the two beakers sideways at eye level. (This will make the effect even more startling.) Then slowly pour vegetable oil into the small container so it overflows into the larger one. Ask your friend to give you a shout if they see anything change. As you continue to pour in the oil, something remarkable happens: the small Pyrex beaker starts to disappear, from the bottom up. When the oil is halfway up the sides of the smaller beaker, stop and check it out again. The part of the smaller beaker below the level of the oil will be invisible, while the part above the oil, will look the same. Continue pouring oil until the smaller beaker is completely covered. It will simply vanish!

This trick will work best if your smaller beaker is completely clear, without any writing or markings on it.

## IN CONCLUSION

Light reflects off objects. That's actually the reason we can see them—it's the reason you can read this book. When light moves between different substances (for example, between oil and water) it changes speed, and while some of that light gets reflected as usual, some gets refracted, or bent. Refraction is the reason this experiment works. Scientists have created a refractive index, which assigns refraction rates to different substances. Vegetable oil and Pyrex have almost exactly the same refractive index, which means that light travels through them at an identical speed and is neither reflected nor refracted. Thus, the smaller beaker seems to disappear.

# 36

# WHICH WAY?

## Directions aren't normally as confusing as this!

## SETUP

Draw two arrows on the piece of paper. It doesn't matter whether they point left or right—your choice—as long as they're both pointing in the same direction; leave about ½ inch (1.3cm) between them. Place the piece of paper a few inches behind the glass, taping it to or leaning it against something upright, and look through the glass. Now pour water into the glass to just above the bottom arrow but below the top one. Have another look through the glass and see what's happened.

## TESTING

To make sure you're not just seeing things, add more water to the glass to a point above the second arrow, watching through the glass to see what happens as you do. You'll find the same thing happens to the top arrow. Now slide the glass of water away to one side and look at the arrows again. You could also check out what happens when you change the distance between the glass and the paper.

## IN CONCLUSION

When light moves between different mediums (for example, from air to glass) it changes speed. Some of that light is still reflected, but some is also refracted, meaning it bends, and the amount that it bends is described by the refractive index. (Which we looked at when we make a beaker vanish on page 119.)

When light moves from air, to glass, to air, to glass, the changes cancel each other out and the arrows don't change direction. However, when you add water, you're essentially creating a lens that is curved on the horizontal. When light passes through the water, it gets bent on the horizontal and flips the image so it faces the other way. Hence the confusing change of direction.

Manmade lenses are used in cameras, telescopes, binoculars, and microscopes. You may even be reading this with the aid of a couple—if you wear glasses or contact lenses.

Of course, you don't have to use arrows in your drawing—try experimenting with other images to see what happens.

# #37

# RUBBER EGG

## There's nothing hard-boiled about this experiment!

**YOU WILL NEED:**
- Raw egg • White vinegar
- Glass jar bigger than the egg
- Dessert spoon • Patience!

OPTIONAL:
- Knife • Pushpin • Another raw egg • Toothpick or wooden skewer

## SETUP

Take the egg and place it carefully into the glass jar. Make sure you don't crack the shell. Gently pour white vinegar into the jar until it covers the egg. The egg should be covered by a good inch or so of the vinegar. Now, we wait…

Leave the egg to soak in the vinegar for two days, after which it'll look a bit scummy—certainly not something you'd necessarily want to touch. Lift the egg out of the jar with the spoon and then peel off what remains of the shell. Well, how about that?

**!**

Don't eat this egg. Seriously, don't. It'll be horrible.

## TESTING

Your newly naked egg will behave rather differently from the hard-shelled original model. Mainly, you'll notice that it's become quite squidgy, rubbery even, and now it's possible to bounce the egg on your kitchen table. You'll be able to do this from a height of a couple of inches, though we'd be interested to know what happens if you drop the egg from a greater height. (Actually, we know what happens.)

You can try turning off the lights and shining a flashlight through the egg. When you're done with your observations, empty the vinegar from the jar, pop the egg back inside it, and then poke it with the knife. What happens? Yes, that's why we said to put it back in the jar!

# RUBBER EGG

> Don't ingest the raw egg, as there is a risk of food poisoning.

> If you can't blow the raw egg out of the shell take a toothpick or wooden skewer, poke it through the larger hole, and wiggle it around to break up the yoke.

## ADDITIONAL SETUP

You can also make a few adjustments to this experiment to produce a result that's equally surprising: a foldable eggshell. First, take a raw egg that hasn't been soaked in vinegar and make a small hole with the pushpin in one end of the eggshell. Then do the same at the other end, opposite the first hole, but wiggle it around a bit to make that hole slightly bigger—think about half the diameter of a pencil. By blowing through the smaller hole, you should now be able to force the inside of the egg out through the hole; do this so you have a completely empty eggshell.

Fill the jar about two-thirds full with vinegar again and hold the empty eggshell below the surface so the inside fills with vinegar and it sinks to the bottom. Leave the jar until the shell has broken down—it should take about two days. When your egg is "done," you should be left with just the papery inner membrane. Take this out of the vinegar, being careful to keep the membrane intact. Rinse the egg sleeve carefully in water to remove the vinegar and then toss it gently between your hands to re-inflate it.

You'll now be able to fold the sleeve in half or quarters. When you want to bring it back to full size, just toss it between your hands to inflate it with air again.

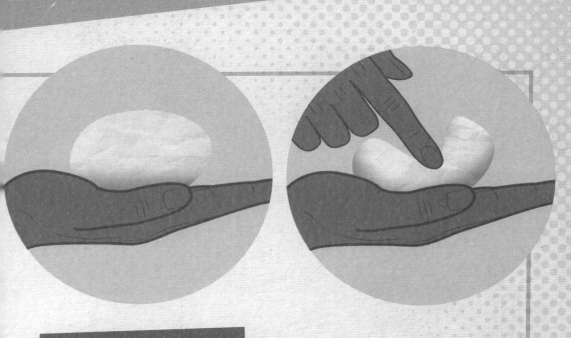

## IN CONCLUSION

When you cover the egg with vinegar you start a chemical reaction that dissolves the shell of the egg, which is made of calcium carbonate. The acetic acid (which makes up about 4 percent of the vinegar) reacts with calcium carbonate and produces carbon dioxide, and this is why you'll see bubbles on the shell of the egg. After two days in the acid, the shell is so weak that it's either dissolved completely or can be rubbed away with your fingers.

You may notice that your egg is slightly larger than before too. This is because the membrane inside the shell is semipermeable, and so some of the vinegar is able to pass through the wall and into the runny part inside. The egg membrane also contains a secret ingredient: keratin, the same stuff that makes up human hair and nails, which helps to explain its toughness—until you poke it with the knife, that is.

If you make the foldable version, the principles are exactly the same, with one important difference: when you toss the empty egg sleeve between your hands, you're forcing air into it, which is why it inflates back to its original size and looks like a real egg.

# FIRE SNAKE

## A snake arises from the flames

> **!**
>
> Please don't use an ordinary lighter for this because it's very easy to get burned. If you haven't got a long-handled barbecue lighter then use a long match or, better still, a taper.

## SETUP

Mix the sugar and baking powder together in the glass and stir them together with the spoon. Give the bowl of sand a good squirt of lighter fluid for five or six seconds, making small circles with your hand as you squeeze. Pour about half the contents of the glass into the center of the bowl of sand, to make a neat little pile—like a squirt of whipped cream on a cake. Set fire to the contents of the bowl with the barbecue lighter and stand far back. It'll take a moment or two but, then, something incredible will happen.

Make sure you do this experiment on an open area of your kitchen floor or table, well away from anything flammable.

## TESTING

At first, it will seem as though the lighter fluid is burning, and that the mixture of sugar and baking soda is starting to scorch, but nothing much else is happening. Then, suddenly, the reaction starts, picks up speed and strange, twisted shapes emerge out of the fire. Quite soon, the "fire snakes" will become too big for the bowl and convulse out over the edges, but they'll keep coming, forming distorted shapes until the sugar and baking soda mixture is exhausted. At the end, you'll be left with something that looks like a gnarled tree branch that's been consumed in a terrible forest fire. It really is quite amazing to watch. The whole process should take about 20 minutes from when you first light the fluid.

If you create the giant version (see ADDITIONAL SETUP on page 129) you'll find that the snake looks less like a snake and more like a volcano, as it mimics the hollow shape of the baking soda and sugar mixture.

If you try making the giant snake we recommend you conduct this part of the experiment outside because, if it works, it's going to make quite a mess.

## ADDITIONAL SETUP

It's possible to produce a giant version of this experiment by keeping the relative quantities of sugar to baking soda at four-to-one and increasing the size of the bowl, the amount of sand, and the amount of lighter fluid accordingly.

If you're disappointed with the size or proportions of your giant fire snake, try arranging the baking soda and sugar mix in a slightly different way. Instead of simply pouring it onto the lighter fluid-soaked sand to make a mound, turn it into a hollow—like the sides of a volcano. This will allow the fire to heat the mixture from both inside and outside the walls and will help to inflate your snake even more.

## IN CONCLUSION

Heat is the driver behind three separate chemical reactions that combine to create this remarkable experiment and allow the fire snake to form. In reaction number one, sugar burns in the presence of oxygen to produce carbon dioxide and water vapor. This pulls the mixture of sugar and baking soda upward. At the same time, reaction number two occurs. After the initial burn, the sugar continues to heat up, but there's not enough oxygen for it to burn any longer so, instead, something called thermal decomposition occurs. This is the chemical breakdown of a substance caused by heat, and a product of the reaction is the solid carbon that makes up most of the body of the snake. Finally, we get reaction number three, in which the baking soda also decomposes in the heat, to produce solid sodium carbonate, loads of carbon dioxide, and water vapor.

The combined products of these three reactions puff the mixture up, helping it to expand and inflate to produce the distinctive snake shape. Indeed, the force of the chemical reactions are strong enough to push the mixture up and out of the bowl.

What part does the sand play in all this? Interestingly, it doesn't react with anything as such; instead, it helps to distribute the heat from the burning sugar and bicarbonate of soda more evenly, slowing it down and producing a longer fire snake. Without the presence of sand, it would all be over much more quickly.

# #39
# PLASTIC FROM MILK

## Milk is harder than it looks

**YOU WILL NEED:**
- Large cup • Milk • Small saucepan • Jug • White vinegar • Tablespoon • Sieve or strainer • Paper towel • Plastic lunchbox (or another small container)

OPTIONAL:
- Molds • Cookie cutters • Food dye • Chain or cord

## SETUP

Gently heat a cup of milk in a saucepan on the stove until it's warm but not hot. (You can also do this in a plastic bowl in the microwave—just be careful not to overheat it.) Pour the warmed milk into the jug. Add a single tablespoon of white vinegar to the milk and then start stirring. You'll need to be patient with this, because it can take a while, but stir vigorously for a few minutes and you'll start to see a change: that lovely, creamy milk will transform into something rather different.

For every cup of milk you need to add one tablespoon of vinegar. In this way you can easily scale up the experiment if you'd like to make more "plastic."

## TESTING

As you stir the milk and vinegar mixture, it starts to separate until it looks rather like milk that's gone bad—thanks to the vinegar it won't smell terribly nice either. Keep stirring until you can clearly see the white globs of whatever-it-is floating about in a thin, watery liquid. When you can, you're ready for the next step.

Hold the sieve or strainer over the sink and pour the contents of the jug into it. The liquid will disappear and you should be left with a weird curd-like substance. Leave the sieve over the sink for an hour to drain.

Next take a couple of paper towels and lay them flat on the table, dump the "curds" out onto the towels and fold them over, pressing down to mop up as much of the excess liquid as you can—in order for this experiment to work you need the remains to be as dry as possible.

Finally, tip the curds into a container—we used a small plastic lunchbox because it was convenient, but you can use whatever you like. Press them down as if they were a cake mix or bread dough to form a solid rectangle and make the top as smooth as you can. Pop the whole thing on a windowsill and leave it there to dry for 48 hours. The substance you're left with is called casein (pronounced *kayseen*).

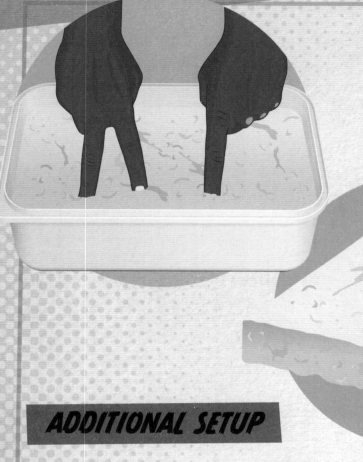

## ADDITIONAL SETUP

Casein has been used in the past to make all kinds of decorative items, and there's nothing to stop you from molding your "plastic" into shapes that are more attractive than our block. While the casein is still soft, you can tear off chunks and push them into a mold (you'll find plenty of inexpensive, reusable silicon molds online) or you could use metal cookie cutters to cut out shapes.

You could even make casein jewelry. If you wanted to make a pendant, for example, you could push the chain into the casein while it's still malleable; then, when it sets, the chain will be firmly embedded and you can decorate the shape itself. Alternatively, poke a hole through the casein shape and you'll be able to thread a chain or cord through later, once it's set.

Adding food dye to the curds and kneading them before they set will color the casein and can produce some interesting marbled effects.

# IN CONCLUSION

Along with whey, casein is one of the two major proteins found in milk. When you add the vinegar you change the acidity of the milk and cause the casein molecules to unravel into long chains; this breakdown is what makes the milk curdle. Warming the milk beforehand excites the molecules, which then move around more quickly, and this accelerates the process.

Casein has been used by humans for a long time. The ancient Egyptians used it as a sort of glue to help fix the pigments they used in giant wall paintings. Before plastic became widely used in the 1940s, casein was often deployed to make everything from beads and buttons to pens, hairbrushes, and the backs of handheld mirrors. Casein is durable, long-lasting, and inexpensive. It's not possible to break a decent-size chunk of casein with your bare hands—it needs a good whack with a hammer to crack it. It has microscopic pockmarks on its surface, which means it can be dyed easily and the color stays strong and true. Innovative casein-makers were able to mimic tortoiseshell and pearl finishes successfully.

Both whey and casein are sold as protein powders to help people trying to build muscle mass. The main difference between the two is that whey is digested very quickly while casein is digested slowly, making it more useful for aiding recovery after a tough workout and reducing muscle breakdown.

# 40

# TAP TAP FREEZE

## Who knew you can freeze water with just one tap?

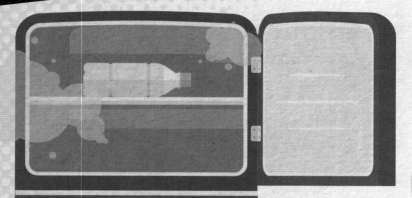

You can make your own purified water by filtering tap water or boiling it for 10 minutes.

## SETUP

Fill your bottle with your purified water, then screw the cap back on and lay it down on its side in the freezer compartment. After about 1 hour and 50 minutes, remove the bottle, being careful not to jar or shake it at all—this is really important. Hold the bottle in one hand and, with the other, give the top a good solid tap on the cap. What on earth is going on?

## TESTING

When you tap the top of the bottle, ice crystals will form like a ball in the middle of the bottle, spreading out until the whole thing is frozen. How long should you leave the water in the freezer? That depends on the size of the bottle and the temperature of the freezer. We found that for a 20oz (50cl) bottle, just under two hours was about right, but you'll have to experiment. You can also try standing a bottle upright in the freezer, then, instead of tapping it, take it out and pour the contents slowly over an ice cube (be careful not to touch the ice cube).

## IN CONCLUSION

Water freezes at 32°F (0°C), right? Well, sort of. Ice crystals start to form at 32°F because the impurities in normal water kick-start the crystallization process, which causes ice to form. But purified water doesn't have these little impurities, so the water molecules don't have anything to grab hold of until the temperature of the water drops much lower—maybe as cold as −40°F (−40°C). Brrr.

When you hit the bottle cap, the energy you generate starts a process called nucleation in the supercooled water, and that's all you need to start the freezing process. Shaking the bottle can have the same effect, so be careful when you take it out of the freezer.

Interestingly, scientists are looking at supercooling as a way of preserving food that doesn't alter its cells as much as conventional freezing. If it works, they believe we won't be able to taste the difference between fresh food and food that's been supercooled and then thawed out.

# #41
# RECORD PLAYER FROM SCRATCH

## Make the world's cheapest record player

**YOU WILL NEED:**
- Old long-playing record (bear in mind that it will get scratched) • Long pin
- Piece of paper • Sticky tape • Pencil • Sticky tack • A helper

If you can't produce sound from your record player try changing the pin for a thinner one—the skinnier the pin is the better the results.

## SETUP

For this experiment you need to use a long pin with a head, rather than a sewing needle. Start by taking your piece of paper and rolling it up to form a cone. You want to make sure the small end of the cone is pretty tight, so don't leave much of a hole in the bottom. Secure the cone using sticky tape so it doesn't flap open. Now you want to push the pin through both sides of the paper at the narrow end of the cone, about an inch (2.5cm) from the bottom. Push it all the way through the cone, at an angle of about 45 degrees. Once it's in place, keep it there by covering the pinhead with a piece of tape.

Work out which side of the long-playing record (LP) you want to listen to and make sure that's facing up. Now take your pencil and sharpen it, and push the pencil—point down—through the hole in the center of the LP. It should fit pretty snugly. If it doesn't you can use a blob of sticky tack on both sides to help keep it in place. It's important that this is a good fit because your friend is going to use the pencil to make the LP spin.

**Make sure you don't touch the rest of the cone while you're holding the end, as this will interfere with the vibrations and reduce the volume.**

# RECORD PLAYER FROM SCRATCH

**If your friend isn't able to spin the LP consistently at a steady speed, cheat: put it on a turntable and try that.**

## TESTING

Get your assistant to turn the pencil so that the LP spins in a clockwise direction. It's important that they try and keep a steady speed, although this isn't always possible. While they do that, take the cone and, holding it by the edge up at the widest end, place the other end, with the pin pointing down, onto the surface of the spinning record. You should immediately hear the sound of whatever's recorded onto the LP, coming out of the larger end of the cone.

## IN CONCLUSION

Sound is made up of vibrating air molecules that travel in waves. These hit your eardrum and resonate the tiny little bones in your inner ear; in turn, these vibrations pass down nerves into the brain where they're interpreted as sound. The greater or fewer the vibrations per second dictates the frequency of the sound, and sound waves have what's called an amplitude, which controls whether your brain hears the sound as soft or loud.

The cone of paper plays an important role in your homemade record player. When you shout, sound is dispersed in a semicircle in front of you (since very little travels out through the back of your head) so it dissipates quickly. When you shout through a cone, however, the sound is channeled in a particular direction and therefore becomes louder and stronger. It's why people cup their hands around their mouths when trying to make themselves heard at a distance. The cone mimics this, taking the vibrations generated when the pin moves through the grooves in the record and amplifying them so you can hear a tinny sound, even without placing your ear at the top of the cone. If you look back at old advertisements for many famous record and hi-fi companies, you'll see a familiar logo showing a dog listening to an old gramophone, which has a cone to disperse sound, just like your homemade record player.

## RECORDING HISTORY

This experiment uses the same principle as the very first record player—the brainchild of that great inventor Thomas Edison, who invented it in 1877. It works by simply amplifying the vibrations that are created when the pin moves through the spiral of tiny ups and downs that are etched into the surface of the LP. Despite many advances in technology, LPs have been made in the same way since the early gramophones, which started to appear about 10 years after Edison's invention. Originally, recordings were created on disks made of rubber, but these were eventually replaced by vinyl, which is more durable.

## #42 ⚠️
# DIY SEALABLE FREEZER BAG

## No sealable bags?
## Make your own!

**YOU WILL NEED:**
- Open-top freezer bags (the kind that don't have a seal)
- Tinfoil • Dish towel • Iron
- Food for freezing

OPTIONAL:
- Ironing board

💡 When you iron over the foil be careful not to touch the plastic of the bag, as this will melt and make a real mess of your iron. And don't linger too long elsewhere either, in case you scorch either the towel or the surface beneath.

## SETUP

With most open-top freezer bags, if you want to seal a bag you'll have to twist the top shut and then secure it with a bendy clip (usually a bit of metal wrapped in plastic). Our way is a lot more efficient. Take your ordinary freezer bag and put the food you want to freeze inside. Press the end of the bag together and fold over. Tear off a strip of tinfoil longer than the width of the bag and about 4in (10cm) wide. Take your towel and place it on a heatproof kitchen counter (or on the ironing board if you're using one). Place the foil on the towel and lay the open end of the freezer bag on the foil. Fold the foil over the end of the bag and fold it shut. Now you're ready to seal the bag.

## TESTING

Make sure the iron is set to a low heat and iron away—just one or two passes over the foil should be enough. Once you're done, turn off the iron and set it aside somewhere safe, and leave everything to cool down for 10 minutes. Once it's cool, take a look at your freezer bag. When you peel away the foil, you'll see that the bag is sealed shut. You've just made your own sealed freezer bag.

## IN CONCLUSION

The science here is simple. Plastic has a lower melting point than the aluminum foil. Plastic starts to melt at around 160°F (71°C), while tinfoil just shrugs heat off until the temperature gets to something like 1200°F (649°C). That means you can melt the plastic bag between the two bits of foil and then leave it to reconstitute itself as it cools down. If you're using a thin bag, you'll notice that the bit you iron over turns to Swiss cheese—it's full of holes. However, as you can see, there's also a clear line where the bag is sealed, thanks to the edge of the iron, meaning that it can be used as a perfectly good freezer bag.

# #43 ⚠

# MUMMIFIED APPLE

## You probably shouldn't eat that...

**YOU WILL NEED:**
- An apple • Salt
- Baking soda • Bowl • Knife
- Good-sized jar

OPTIONAL:
- Second jar • Another apple
- Container large enough to fit a whole apple inside
- Vegetable peeler • Knife
- Wooden skewer

!

It's amazing how many people don't know how to cut an apple safely. You should always make an arch over the apple with your thumb and four fingers and then cut underneath the arch—that way you'll never nick your fingers.

## SETUP

First, cut yourself a quarter of apple using the arch technique described in the "tip" box. Then mix equal amounts of salt and baking soda together in the bowl. To judge how much you need, check out the size of your jar: you want to be able to nearly fill it with a 50/50 mixture of the two, leaving a little room for the section of apple that you'll be mummifying. Pour about an inch of the mixture into the jar and then add the apple quarter. Cover the rest of the apple with the mixture and you're done. Now you just need to set your jar aside in a dry place at room temperature, somewhere neither too hot nor too cold, and wait…

## TESTING

You can leave the apple in the jar for up to two months but, if you're impatient to see what's happened, you can probably make do with only a week, by which time the salt and baking soda will have worked their magic. Scrape out the mixture from the jar to reveal the apple (if you've left it for more than a week you may have to use a knife to do this) and then remove it from the jar. Your apple quarter has been mummified.

# MUMMIFIED APPLE

## ADDITIONAL SETUP

There are a couple of other variations you can try here: one scientific, one more fun. When you prepare the apple quarter to be immersed in the baking soda and salt, take another quarter and put it into another empty jar with no mixture. Then, when you remove the mummified version from the mixture, you'll be able to compare it with the one that was left in its natural state.

Alternatively, take a whole apple and use a vegetable peeler to remove most of the skin, leaving just the skin on top and at the bottom where the core is. Then, carefully, make a face with the knife by cutting out two eyeholes, a nose, and a jagged mouth. After that, you can follow the same process as described in the original setup, though you'll need to use a bigger receptacle to store the whole apple and enough of the salt/baking soda mixture to cover it. When you take it out after a week, your apple will look a bit like a shrunken head. To complete the effect, stick it on a wooden skewer and leave several at the edge of your neighborhood to scare off strangers.

**!**

It should probably go without saying, but a mummified apple isn't the same as a dried apple—so don't eat it.

# IN CONCLUSION

If you place a piece of cut apple in a bowl of salt water, it won't go brown because the salt prevents oxidization from occurring. However, when you mix salt and baking soda you create something quite different. This mixture is a powerful desiccant: a substance that leeches moisture out of the air—or anything else—and absorbs it. It's the same principle that's employed in those small bags filled with silica crystals that often come inside the packaging of electronics. They're designed to do exactly the same job and absorb any moisture that could damage the equipment.

In this experiment, all of the moisture is leeched out of the apple quarter and into the surrounding mixture, leaving you with remains that are shrunken and shriveled. The other thing you'll notice is that the piece of apple doesn't rot. This is because there's no moisture in the jar to allow bacteria to grow; it all gets absorbed by the mixture. If you compare this with an apple quarter that's simply been left in an otherwise empty jar, you'll see that the second apple has gone through decomposition, rather than mummification.

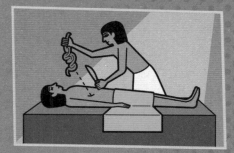

This experiment uses the same principles as the mummification process carried out by ancient Egyptians, possibly as early as 3700 BCE. Like many rituals, it probably began by accident when someone dug up a grave and discovered that a corpse had been preserved by the mixture of sand and air. (Much of Egypt receives no rain.) This then led to the discovery that when sand was mixed with natron (a naturally occurring salt), it had even better hygroscopic (water-absorbing) properties and would preserve a body without decay for thousands of years.

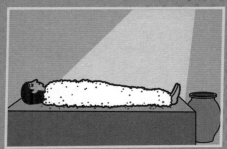

# SMARTPHONE CINEMA

## Make a cardboard box movie theater

**YOU WILL NEED:**
• Smartphone • Magnifying glass • Old shoebox • Large paperclip • Pen or pencil • Electrical tape • Craft knife

OPTIONAL:
• Small hacksaw • Black paper or black paint • Glue

Take the lid off your shoebox and place it on its end. Unscrew the handle of the magnifying glass to leave just the circular glass (or cut the handle off with a hacksaw). Place it on one end of the shoebox, draw around it with the pen/pencil, and then use the craft knife to cut out the circle. You can now affix the magnifying glass over the hole, using the electrical tape to glue it to the outside of the shoebox.

Next, you need to make a stand for your smartphone. You may already own a stand and that should do the trick. It must be easy to slide forward and backward along the inside of the shoebox, and it must allow your phone to stand on its side at 90 degrees. If you look at the illustration here, you'll see one simple way to "build" (or bend) a stand out of a large paperclip. If you don't fancy trusting dollars' worth of advanced technology to a cheap paperclip, then there are all sorts of other DIY solutions you could use. We've seen them made from cardboard, craft sticks, even plastic cups. Another ingenious idea is to make one out of plastic building blocks.

If you're having trouble getting the paperclip to work as a stand, or if you have a larger smartphone, try using a couple of binder clips. Just search online for "smartphone stand binder clips" and you'll find plenty of ideas.

## TESTING

Turn your smartphone on and load up a video that you'd like to watch. Now place it inside the shoebox, making sure the screen is pointing at the magnifying glass and the phone is at a 90-degree angle on its stand. Put the lid back on the shoebox and turn the box so the magnifying glass is facing a blank wall.

OK, you've done all this, so how come the image looks so awful and why—more to the point—is it upside down?

Let's fix these things in order. First, stop the film. Second, turn your phone's screen brightness to the highest setting. Third, find the control on your phone that stops the screen from auto-rotating. This is important because you're going to place the phone back in the box *upside down* and this will stop the screen from righting itself again.

Next, do your best to make sure the room is as dark as possible and then place the shoebox on a table, pointed at a section of blank wall. You'll now need to experiment a bit to get the picture sharp. Start by placing the shoebox at the end of the table farthest from the wall and then slowly slide it forward until the picture comes into focus. Once you've done that, experiment with moving the smartphone up and down inside the shoebox until the picture is nice and sharp.

## ADDITIONAL SETUP

There's one more thing you can do to improve the quality of the image produced by your smartphone cinema. If the insides of your shoebox aren't black, measure out the bottom, top and walls of the box and then cut out pieces of black paper matching these dimensions. Glue these to the inside of the box. Alternatively, you could paint the inside of the box black. The color black is really good at absorbing light, so it will help to ensure that any light produced by the phone's screen comes out through the magnifying glass and doesn't leak out into the box.

## IN CONCLUSION

A convex lens—such as your magnifying glass—makes objects look larger because it disperses light. When objects are within the focal length of the lens, they appear larger, but when they are further away, they will appear smaller and inverted. You can test this for yourself by holding a pencil upright in one hand and a magnifying glass in the other. Look at the pencil through the lens close up and then move it away from the lens until it comes into focus. Keep moving it away and there'll come a point at which the pencil turns upside down. That's exactly what happens to the image being projected from the phone. This is why the phone has to be upside down, so that the image on the wall will be the right way up.

Bizarrely, the same thing happens to light entering your eyes. They see everything upside down, but your brain corrects this and changes the orientation for you.

**Once you've found the correct position for your projector, make a little mark there so you can find it next time you fancy a night in at the cinema.**

# #45

MINING FOR IRON

## Proof that some cereal really is enriched with iron

**YOU WILL NEED:**
• Iron-fortified cereal (such as cornflakes) • Large bowl
• Potato masher • Hot water
• Spoon • Sealable freezer bag
• Neodymium magnet
OPTIONAL:
• Different iron-fortified breakfast cereals

Feeling particularly lazy today? Instead of mashing the cereal by hand, you can just pop it in a blender for 20 seconds.

Pour a breakfast bowl-size portion of cereal into your bowl and then crush it up with the potato masher. You want to get it as powdery as you can. Next, add a cup of hot water and stir the mixture with a spoon. What you're hoping to end up with is a mixture that looks a bit like soggy oatmeal—add more water if necessary. Once you're happy with your mixture, pour it into the bag. Squeeze the air from the bag and seal it shut. Next, lay the bag flat on the table and spread the mixture out evenly with your fingers. Then, take the magnet and, starting at one end, slowly stroke the bag down to the other. Imagine the bag is a swimming pool with invisible lanes: stroke the magnet down the first lane a few times, then do the same to the second lane, and so on, until you've covered the whole bag. Be sure to move the magnet in the same direction each time.

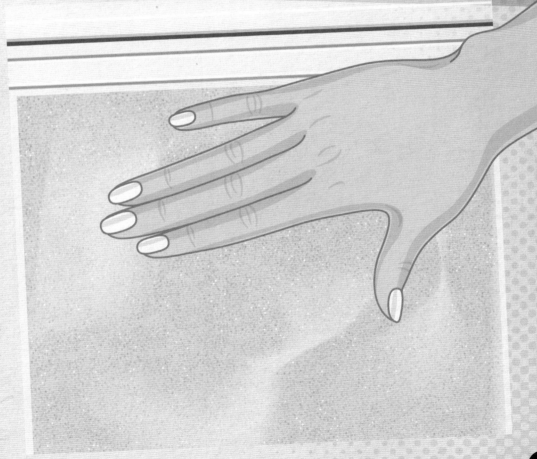

## TESTING

After you've stroked the magnet down the bag about 30 or 40 times, stop and have a look. You should be able to see tiny dark specks in the cereal. If you can't, try another 20 or so strokes and look again. When you see them, all lined up along the bottom of the bag, use the magnet to sweep them together, so they're all gathered together in one corner of the bag. You'll find you've collected a surprising amount of iron, so much, in fact, that you may even be able to lift the corner of the bag off the kitchen table using the magnet. Impressive, eh?

If you like, you can snip off that corner of the bag, tip the contents out onto a plate, and leave the cereal to dry. When it's dry, you'll be able to pick up the iron with your magnet. In a typical bowl of fortified cereal, there'll be about 0.13 grains (8.1mg) of iron.

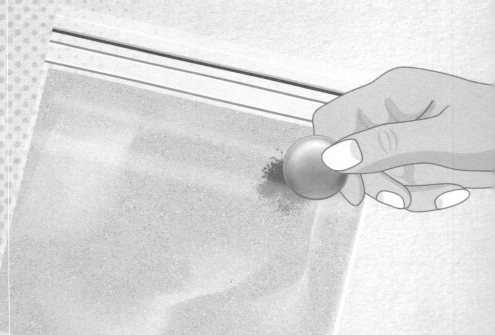

## ADDITIONAL SETUP

Try repeating the test with different cereals to see if you get different results. Check first to make sure that they actually contain iron and then compare the results you get with the levels of iron claimed on the cereal boxes. Which contains the most?

This experiment works best if you use a powerful neodymium magnet, rather than an ordinary magnet. Neodymium magnets are much stronger and therefore better suited to extracting the tiny pieces of iron from the cereal.

## IN CONCLUSION

This is one of those rare "exactly-what-it-says-on-the-box" moments in the book, because when your cereal box tells you that it's fortified with vitamins and iron, it's not kidding. Those flakes of corn (or whatever you've chosen) really are fortified with vitamins and iron; it's just that most of the time, you can't see them. By breaking down the flakes into a powder and then adding the water, you free the iron from the flakes, so it's floating in suspension. Then, it's a simple matter to use the magnet to "mine" the iron into the corner of the bag.

Why does the body need iron in the first place? The basic answer is to help move oxygen to the different parts of the body that need it. The more complex answer is that iron is a key component in hemoglobin, which is the stuff in red blood cells that carries oxygen from your lungs around the body. If you don't have enough iron in your diet, then your body isn't able to make enough red blood cells, which means there are fewer hemoglobin "Ubers" in which oxygen can hitch a ride. That's why people who are lacking in iron complain of feeling tired all the time. Iron is also important for maintaining healthy nails, hair, and skin, so it's vital that you get enough.

# GLOSSARY

Don't speak science? Here's our handy guide to the technical terms used in this book.

**Adhesion**—when something sticks to a surface or to another object

**Aerodynamics**—the study of how solid objects move most efficiently through the air around them

**Amplitude**—describes the height of the crest of a sound wave

**Auxins**—hormones that control the speed at which plant cells grow

**Capillary action**—describes how liquid can flow against gravity in confined spaces

**Center of gravity**—the imaginary point at which weight is evenly dispersed and all sides of an object are in balance, used in physics to help with certain calculations

**Chain reaction**—where one thing happens as a consequence of another thing, which happens as a consequence of another thing, and so on

**Cohesion**—when particles of the same substance stick together

**Combustion chamber**—a confined space where combustion occurs, like an engine

**Combustion triangle**—the three things necessary for fire: heat, fuel, and oxygen

**Compaction**—what happens when a force acts on a material to make it denser

**Condensation**—what happens when a gas cools and turns into a liquid

**Conductor**—something that allows something else (or a force) to pass through it

**Convection**—the tendency of anything hot to move in a circular motion as hotter molecules rise and cooler ones fall

**Crystallization**—technique used to reconstitute a solid material that has been dissolved in liquid to make a solution

**Density**—measured as the mass of something divided by the volume it takes up

**Dessicant**—a substance that is very good at absorbing moisture

**Equilibrium**—when opposing forces acting on an object are balanced, they are said to be "in equilibrium"

**Fluid dynamics**—the study of fluids and how they are affected by external forces

**Force**—the effect one thing can have on another; a force usually pushes or pulls

**Friction**—describes the resistance that occurs when one object rubs across the surface of another

**Gravity**—the force attracting objects to other objects that have greater mass

**Hygroscopic**—describes something that's good at absorbing water

**Implosion**—the opposite of explosion

**Inertia**—the tendency of something to either do nothing or carry on doing whatever it's doing

**Kinetic energy**—energy expressed by something that's moving

**Mass**—like weight, but different; mass describes the amount of matter that makes up an object

**Molecule**—a collection of atoms bound together

**Non-Newtonian liquid**—a liquid that doesn't behave in the same constant way that ordinary liquids behave

**Non-polar molecule**—a molecule where any electrical charge is evenly distributed across the molecule

**Nucleation**—the initial process that takes place when a crystal is formed from a solution, liquid, or vapor

**Particle**—the tiniest unit of matter

**Photosynthesis**—the process by which plants combine sunshine with carbon dioxide and water to produce nutrients

**Phototropism**—the way a plant grows—usually—toward sunlight

**Polar molecule**—a molecule that has a positive "end" and a negative "end"

**Potential energy**—stored energy waiting to be released

**Pressure**—constant physical force exerted against something

**Refracted light**—the way light bends when it moves from one medium to another

**Refractive index**—a way of measuring how light bends when moving between different mediums

**Static electricity**—stationary electrical charge, usually caused by friction

**Supercooled**—describes a liquid cooled to below its freezing point that still remains a liquid

**Supersaturated**—a solution that contains more dissolved material in it than is usually possible, typically as a resulted of being heated

**Surface tension**—describes the elasticity of liquid that clings together to form the smallest possible surface

**Suspension**—a liquid that contains solid matter that may be too small to see with the naked eye

**Thermal decomposition**—when something decomposes as a result of being heated

**Thermal expansion**—when something changes shape or size as a result of being heated

**Thrust**—the movement of mass in a specific, single direction

**Vacuum**—any space that has no matter in it

# FURTHER READING

Has your interest been piqued? If so, here's our handy curated guide to resources—in print and online—that you'll need to build your very own science library.

## BOOKS

**Beattie, Rob.** *101 Incredible Experiments for the Shed Scientist*. London: Ebury Press, 2006

**Bodanis, David.** *E=mc²: A Biography of the World's Most Famous Equation*. New York, NY: Berkley Trade, 2000

**Bryson, Bill.** *A Short History of Nearly Everything*. London: Black Swan, 2016

**Dolnick, Edward.** *The Clockwork Universe: Isaac Newton, the Royal Society, and the Birth of the Modern World*. New York, NY: Harper, 2011

**Ignotofsky, Rachel.** *Women in Science: 50 Fearless Pioneers Who Changed the World*. Emeryville, CA: Ten Speed Press, 2016

**Malpass, Brian.** *The Bluffer's Guide to Science*. London: Oval Books, 2006

**Miodownik, Mark.** *Stuff Matters: Exploring the Marvelous Materials that Shape our Man-Made World*. Boston, MA: Houghton Mifflin Harcourt, 2014

**Phillips, Charles.** *Backyard Physics*. New York, NY: Metro Books

**Shapin, Steven.** *The Scientific Revolution*. Chicago, IL: University of Chicago Press, 1998

## WEBSITES

**Wikipedia Timeline of Scientific Discoveries in the Classical Age**
https://en.wikipedia.org/wiki/Timeline_of_scientific_discoveries
A useful what-happened-when overview of scientific discoveries through the ages

**"5 Mind-Bending Magnet Experiments That Might Surprise You"**
www.techeblog.com/5-mind-bending-magnet-experiments-that-might-surprise-you
Discover more about the properties of powerful neodymium magnets

**"INSANE Stick Bomb Chain Reactions!"** https://www.youtube.com/watch?v=ujDY9vwnne4
Eye-opening examples of how to take your ninja stick bombs to the next level

**Chemistry World** www.chemistryworld.com
Requires registration, but it's worth it for the mix of news, comments, and focus on how chemistry impacts everyday life

**Popular Science** www.popsci.com
An assortment of scientific info—try the random "roll the dice" option

**Ben Goldacre's Bad Science** www.badscience.net

When it comes to skewering poor science, Dr. Goldacre is the best

**How Stuff Works** https://science.howstuffworks.com

Refreshing, practical analysis of what makes the world—and everything in it—tick

**Bill Nye, the Science Guy** www.billnye.com

Breezy videos, explainers and experiments from America's favorite scientist

**Science Daily** www.sciencedaily.com

A daily dose of up-to-date news and the latest scientific discoveries

## PUZZLER ANSWERS

**p.19:** Try putting one or two coins inside the balloon before inflating it.

**p.23:** Fooled you. Larger versions made of tissue paper don't fly any further. Any extra lift generated by the larger volume of hot air is offset by the increased weight of the ash produced by burning something bigger.

**p.29:** Tail fins help with direction and stability. They keep the rocket on course and stop it wobbling about all over the place so it flies further.

**p.39:** The third law of motion: For every action there is an equal and opposite reaction.

**p.83:** Initially, a metal utensil will have the same effect, but because metal is a great conductor of heat, it will quickly reach a similar temperature to the bubbles and the pot will boil over.

**p.91:** Although there'll be a reaction, it won't be as strong as when you use full-fat milk because the latter contains more fat molecules.

# INDEX

# NOTES